Dandelion Reade

Reading and Spelling Activities
Initial Code
Sam - Book 1

Phonic Books Ltd
www.phonicbooks.co.uk

Introduction

The activities in this pack are designed to develop the underlying skills needed to become a fluent reader and speller. They offer a variety of multisensory exercises which include: sound/letter correspondence, segmenting, blending, reading and comprehension, writing and/or dictation.

The purpose of these activities is to help the reader to become 'an expert' at every level before moving onto the next level (unit). The reader then enjoys success at each level, grows in confidence and is motivated to continue learning to read and spell.

The teacher can select which and how many activities the learner needs before moving on to the next level.

The words for each activity can be found on the contents page for that unit.

The activities in this book are based on the stories the children have read in Book 1 set - 'Sam'. Children enjoy activities based on familiar stories they have already read.

Further practice for learners working at a slower pace can be found in the Reading and Writing activity pack for sets 2 and 3 'A Mat' and 'Sit Sam'.

Dandelion Readers Tick Chart

Sam (Book 1)

Title	✓
1. Sam	
2. Pip	
3. Nan	
4. Bad Cat	
5. Bun in the Sun	
6. Zig and Zog	
7. Bob is not Well	
8. The Lost Box	
9. Flip and Flop Slip	
10 The Stink	

www.phonicbooks.co.uk - enquiries@phonicbooks.co.uk

Dandelion Readers

This folder belongs to

____

Dandelion Readers
from
Phonic Books Ltd

Worksheets for Unit 1 - Sam

Page 1 - Sound cards a, i, m, s, t
Page 2 - Cut and glue sounds to make words
Under pictures
Words: Sam- mat - sit
Page 3 - Fill in the missing sounds
Words: Sam - sit
Page 4- Matching upper case to lower case letters
Page 5- Matching lower case to upper case letters
Page 6- Game

Each sheet has its own instructions.

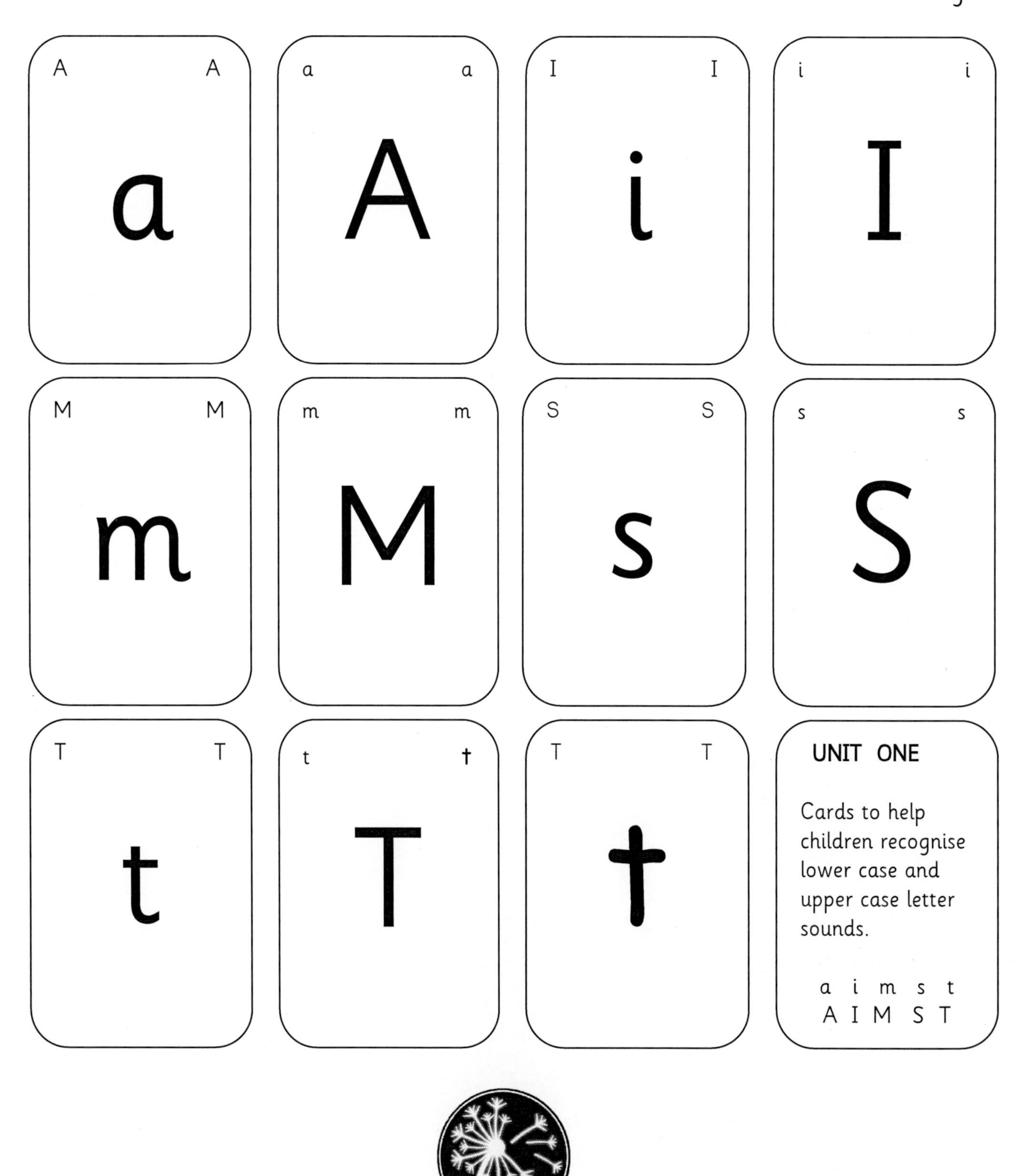

Lower case and upper case letters for Unit 1 – Photocopy the page onto card and cut out the cards.
Two variations of 't' presented to choose appropriate one.
Game 1: Say the sounds and match the pairs.
Game 2: Place the cards face down on the table. Players take turns to turn up two cards and say the sounds. If the same sound is on both cards the player keeps them. If the cards do not represent the same sound, the player replaces the cards face down and the next player has a turn. The winner is the one with the most pairs of cards!

Name: Date: Unit 1 Page 2

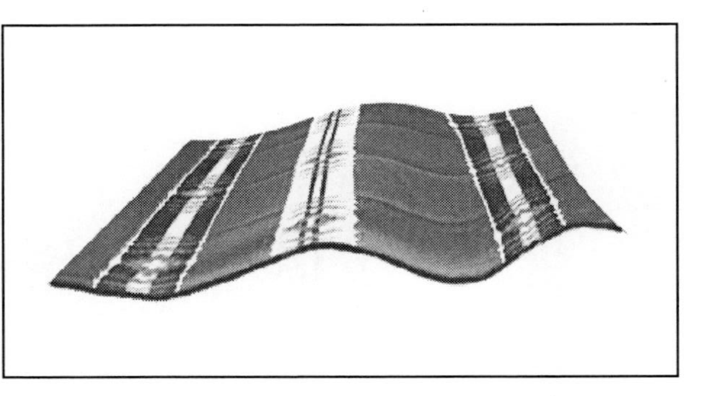

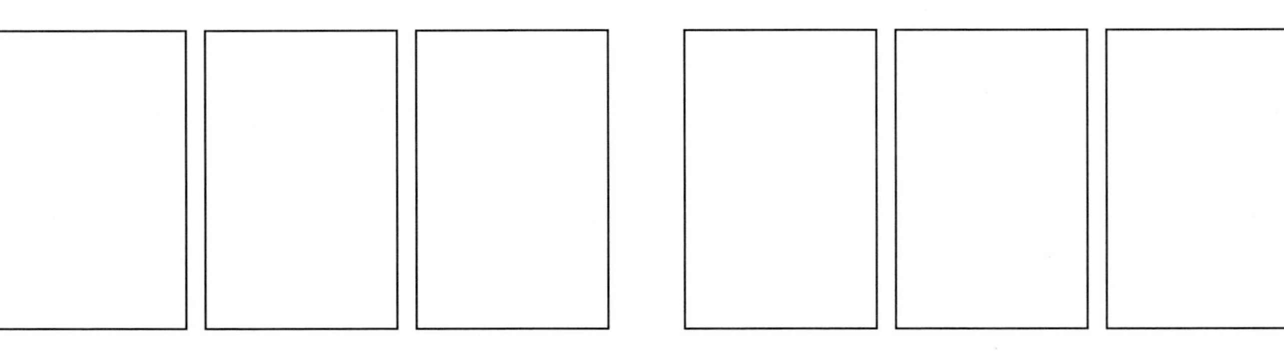

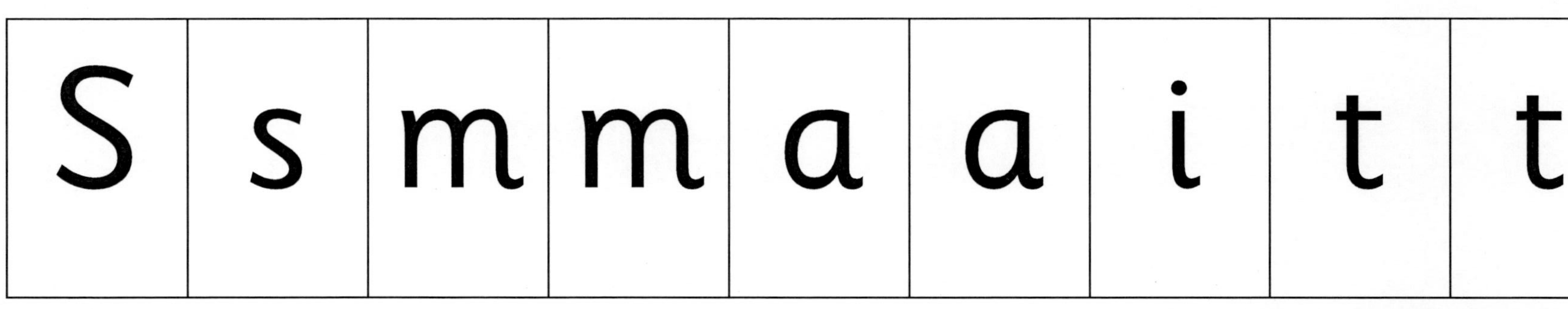

S	s	m	m	a	a	i	t	t

Segmenting and blending exercise. Teacher or child to cut out the individual letters. Ask the child to name the picture and then segment the word into its individual sounds. Teacher to help by saying the word each picture represents if necessary. Ask the child to place the letters in correct sequence under the picture as he says the sounds of the word. Then ask the child to blend the sounds together to read the word.

Name: Date:

Sam

S _ m

_ a _

_ _ _

sit

s _ t

_ i _

_ _ _

Fill in the missing sounds. Say the sounds as you write.

Name: Date:

A	I	M	S	T
a	i	m	s	t

a	i	m

s	t

A I M S T

Match capital letters to lower case letters by cutting and pasting . Child to say the sound of the letters whilst doing the activity.

Name: Date:

A a	I i	M m	S s	T t

A	I	M

S		T

a i m s t

Match lower case letters to capital letters by cutting and pasting . Child to say the sound of the letters whilst doing the activity.

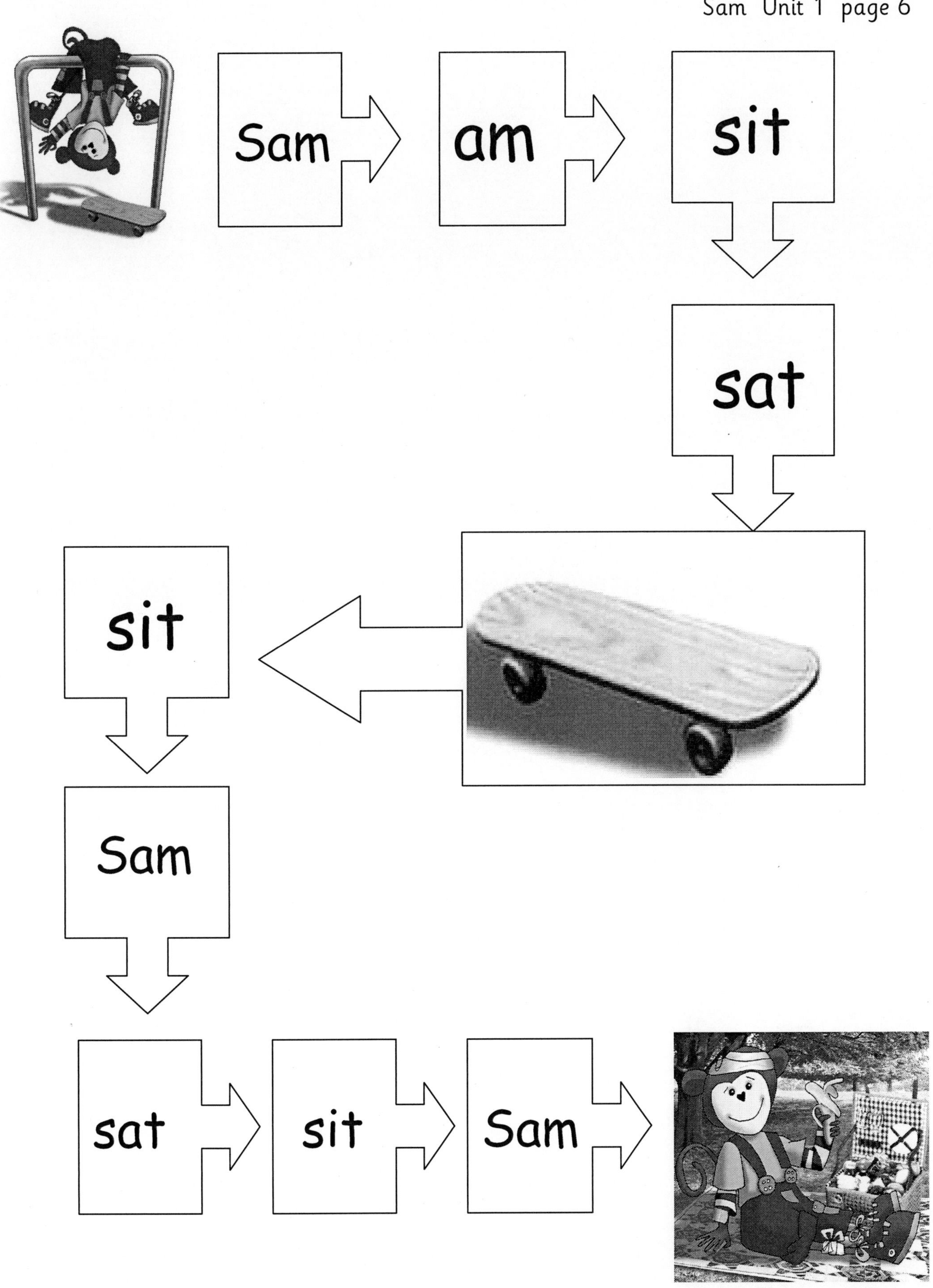

Game for unit 1 book 1 'Sam'. Use a dice with low numbers on it.
(1,1,2,2,0,0 or +1,+1,-1,-1,0,+2)

Dandelion Readers
from
Phonic Books Ltd

Worksheets for Unit 2 - Pip

Page 1 - Sound cards n, p, o

Words for next 5 sheets:
pot, mop, top, tin, pan, Pip

Page 2 - Fill in the missing last sound.
Page 3 - Fill in the missing first sound.
Page 4 - Fill in the missing medial sound.
Page 5 - Fill in the missing initial and final sound
Page 6 - Fill in all the sounds
Page 7 - Match upper case to lower case letters
Page 8 - Match lower case to upper case letters
Page 9 - Reading, cutting and pasting
Page 10 - Cutting, pasting, writing (right handers)
Page 11 - Cutting, pasting, writing (left handers)
Page 12 - Game

Each sheet has its own instructions.

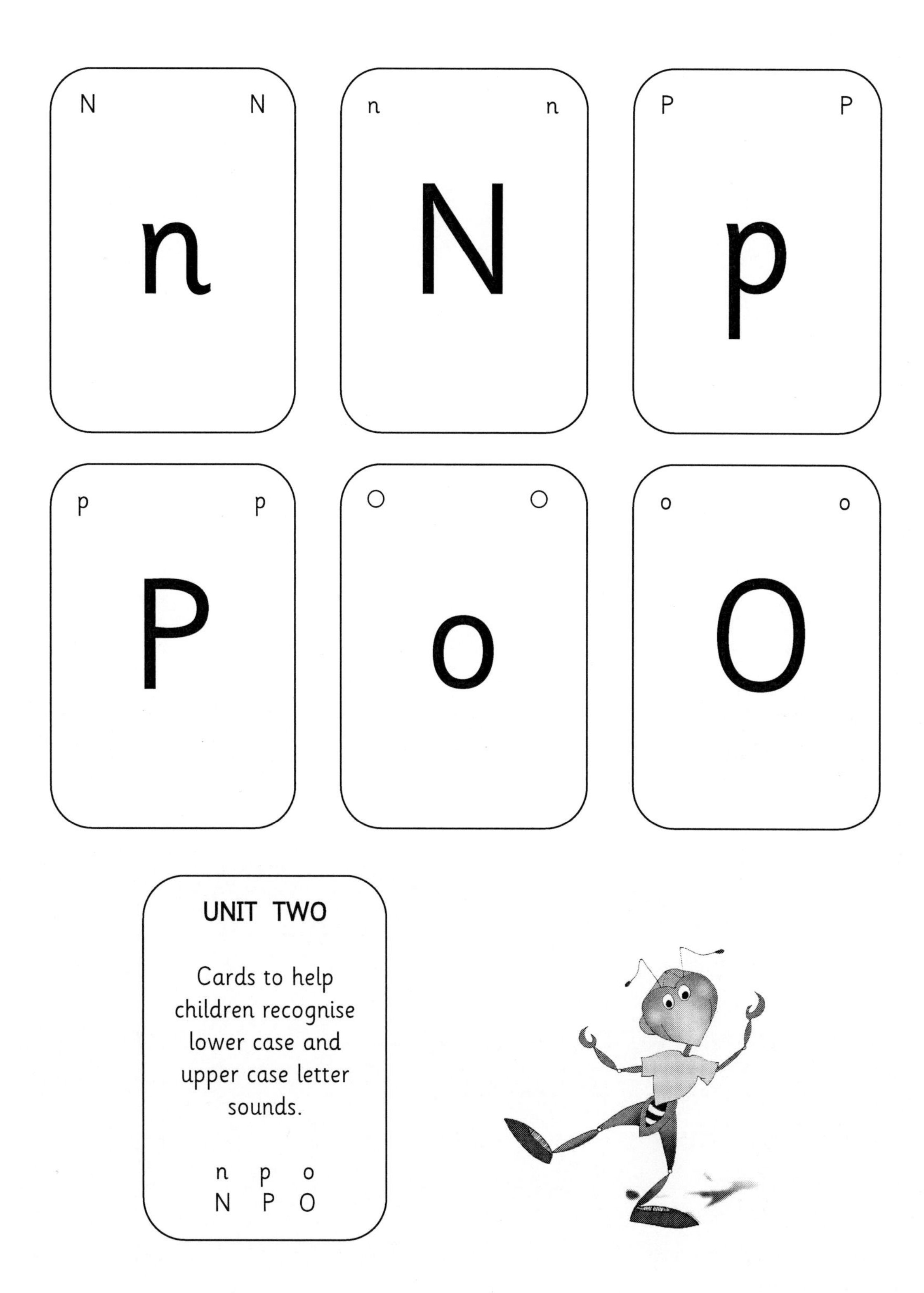

Lower case and upper case letters for Unit 2. These can be added to letters from Unit 1. Photocopy the page onto card and cut out the cards.
Game 1: Say the sounds and match the pairs.
Game 2: Place the cards face down on the table. Players take turns to turn up two cards and say the sounds. If the same sound is on both cards the player keeps them. If the cards do not represent the same sound, the player replaces the cards face down and the next player has a turn. The winner is the player with the most pairs of cards!

Name: Date:

p o _

m o _

t o _

t i _

p a _

P i _

Fill in the missing final sounds. Offer the word if the child has difficulty.

Name: Date:

_ o t

_ o p

_ o p

_ i n

_ a n

_ i p

Fill in the missing initial sounds. Offer the word if the child has difficulty.

Name: Date:

p _ t

m _ p

t _ p

t _ n

p _ n

P _ p

Fill in the missing medial sounds. Offer the word if the child has difficulty.

Name: Date:

_ o _ _ o _

_ o _ _ i _

_ a _ _ i _

Fill in the missing initial and final sounds. Offer the word if the child has difficulty.

Name: Date:

_ _ _ _ _ _

_ _ _ _ _ _

_ _ _ _ _ _

Fill in the missing sounds. Ask the children to say the sounds as they write the words.
Some children may need to be told the words for this sheet.

Name: Date:

N	I	O	P	T
n	i	o	p	t

P	O	T

N	I

n i o p t

Match lower case letters to capital letters letters by cutting and pasting . Child to say the sound of the letters whilst doing the activity.

Name: Date:

A	N	M	P	O
a	n	m	p	o

o

p

m

n

a

A N M P O

Match capital letters to lower case letters by cutting and pasting . Child to say the sound of the letters whilst doing the activity.

Name: Date:

Pip is on the mop.

Pip is in the pan.

Pip is in the pot.

Pip is on the tin.

Reading, cutting and pasting.

Name: Date:

Pip on mop in pan .

the is

Cutting, pasting, reading and writing. (For right handed children)
Ask the child to say the sentence and then sound out the words whilst writing.
The child may need help with 'the' and 'is' as some of these sounds may not have been taught yet.

Name: Date:

Pip on mop in pan .

the is

Cutting, pasting, reading and writing. (For left handed children)
Ask the child to say the sentence and then sound out the words whilst writing.
The child may need help with 'the' and 'is' as some of these sounds may not have been taught yet.

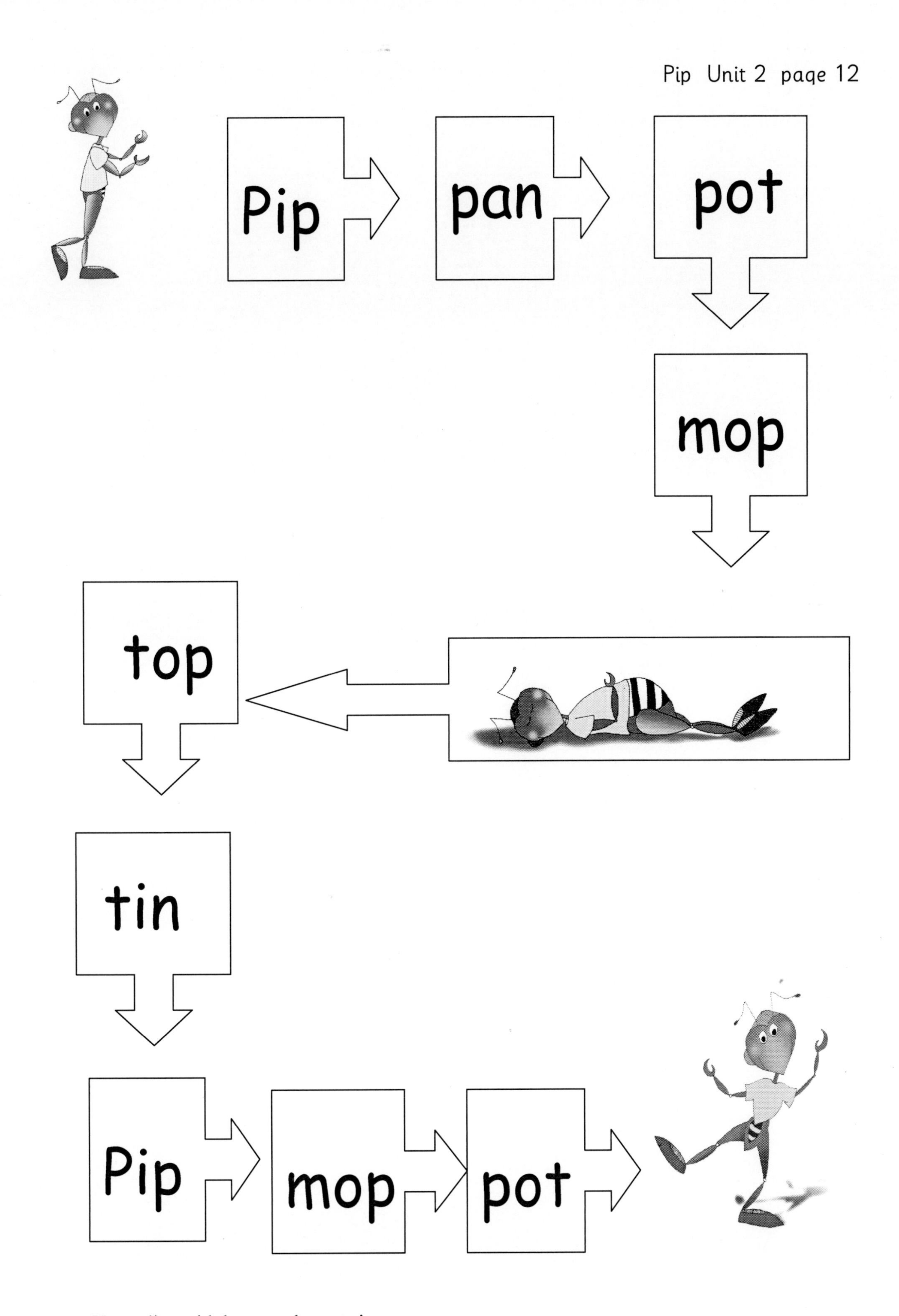

Use a dice with low numbers on it.
(1,1,2,2,0,0 or +1,+1,-1,-1,0,+2)

Dandelion Readers
from
Phonic Books Ltd

Worksheets for Unit 3 - Nan

Page 1 - Sound cards b, c, d, h

Words for next 5 sheets:
bag, hat, cat, pot, Nan, bat

Page 2 - Fill in the missing last sound.
Page 3 - Fill in the missing first sound.
Page 4 - Fill in the missing medial sound.
Page 5 - Fill in the missing initial and final sounds
Page 6 - Fill in all the sounds
Page 7 - Match lower case to upper case letters
Page 8 - Match upper case to lower case letters
Page 9 - Reading, cutting and pasting
Page 10 - Cutting, pasting, writing (right handers)
Page 11 - Cutting, pasting, writing (left handers)
Page 12 - Game

Each sheet has its own instructions.

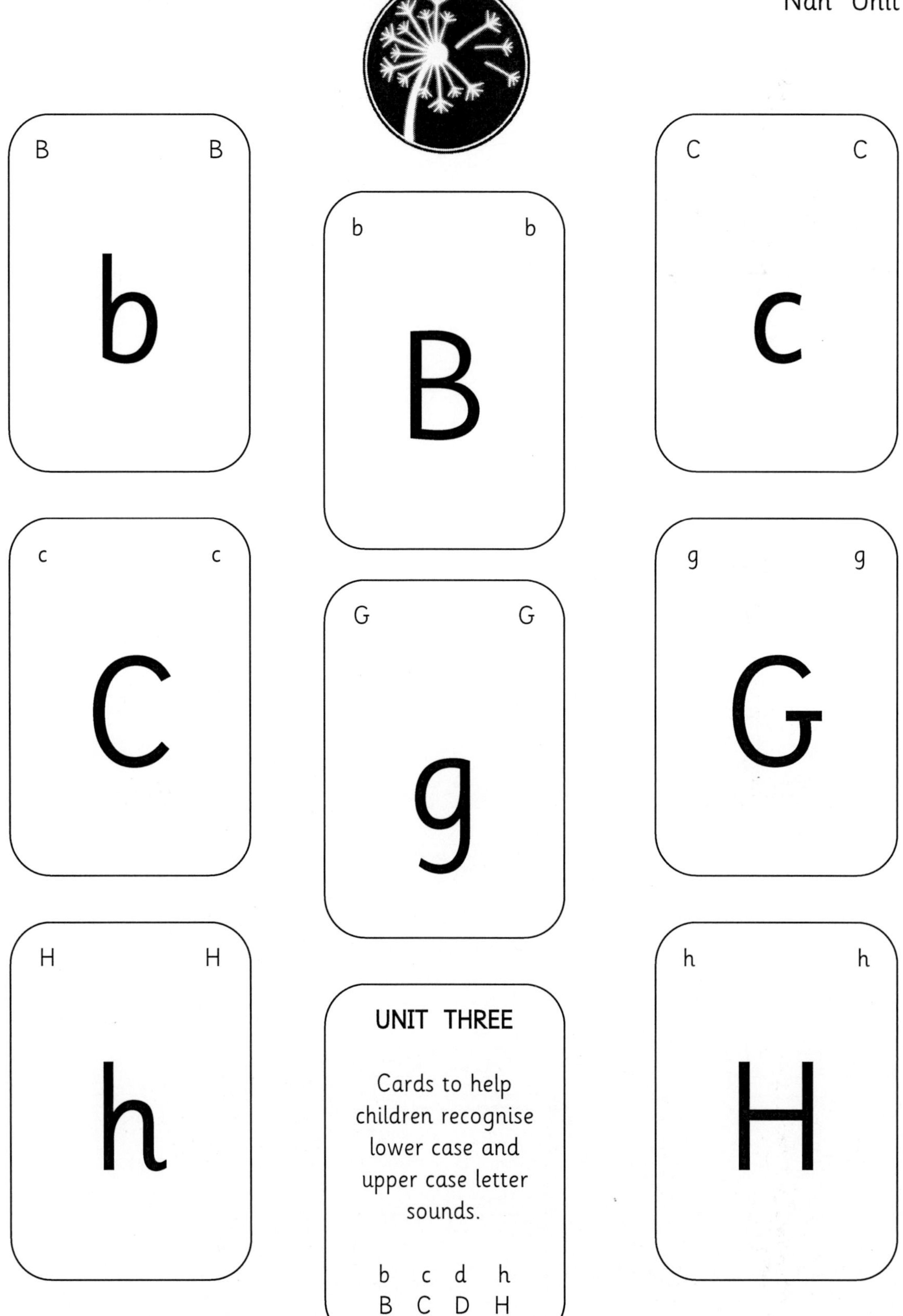

Lower case and upper case letters for Unit 3. These can be added to letters from Units 1 and 2.
Photocopy the page onto card and cut out the cards.
Game 1: Say the sounds and match the pairs.
Game 2: Place the cards face down on the table. Players take turns to turn up two cards and say the sounds. If the same sound is on both cards the player keeps them. If the cards do not represent the same sound, the player replaces the cards face down and the next player has a turn. The winner is the player with the most pairs of cards!

Name: Date:

b a _

h a _

c a _

p o _

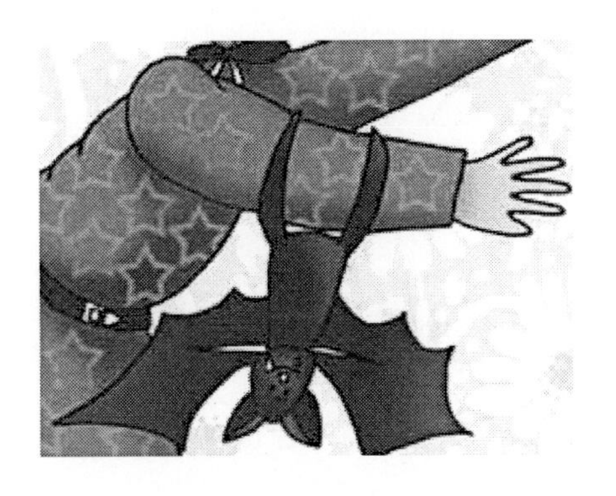

N a _

b a _

Fill in the missing final sounds.
Offer the word if the child has difficulty. Ask child to say the sound when writing.

Name: Date:

_ a g

_ a t

_ a t

_ o t

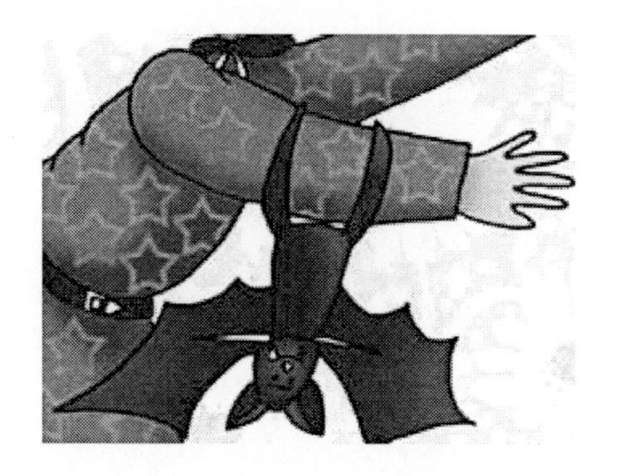

_ a n

_ a t

Fill in the missing initial sounds.
Offer the word if the child has difficulty. Ask child to say the sound when writing.

Name: Date:

b _ g

h _ t

c _ t

p _ t

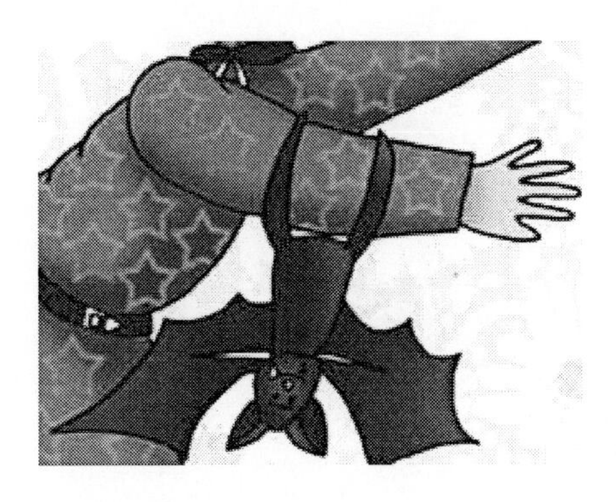

N _ n

b _ t

Fill in the missing medial sounds.
Offer the word if the child has difficulty. Ask child to say the sound when writing.

Name: Date:

_ a _

_ a _

_ a _

_ o _

_ a _

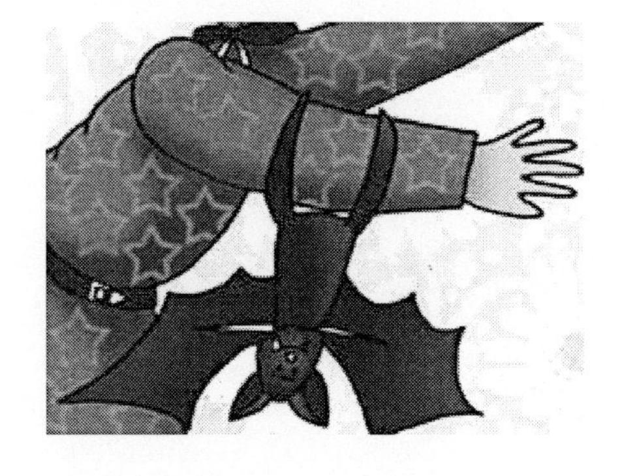

_ a _

Fill in the missing initial and final sounds.
Offer the word if the child has difficulty. Ask child to say the sound when writing.

Name:  Date: Nan Unit 3 page 6

_ _ _ _ _ _

_ _ _ _ _ _

_ _ _ _ _ _

Fill in the missing sounds.
Offer the word if the child has difficulty. Ask child to say the sounds when writing.

Name: Date:

G g	B b	C c	P p	H h

H	G	P

B	C

c	h	b	p	g

Match lower case letters to capital letters by cutting and pasting. Child to say the sound of the letters whilst doing the activity.

Name: Date:

G g	B b	C c	P p	H h

h	g	p

b	c

C H B P G

Match capital letters to lower case letters by cutting and pasting. Child to say the sound of the letters whilst doing the activity.

Name: Date:

The cat is in the bag.

Nan has got a pot.

Nan has got a hat.

The bat is in the bag.

Unit 3 Book 1 'Nan' Reading, cutting and pasting.

Name: Date: Nan Unit 3 page 10

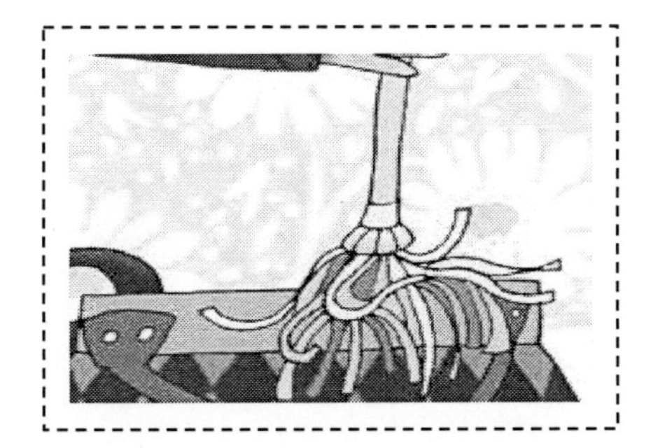

cat Nan got bag big in mop

a the has

Cutting, pasting, writing. (For right handed pupils). The teacher may choose not to provide the words below the pictures.
Ask the child to say the sentence and then sound out the words when writing.
The child may need help with <a, the, has> as some of the sounds may not have been taught yet.

cat Nan got bag big in mop

a the has

Cutting, pasting, writing. (For left handed pupils). The teacher may choose not to provide the words below the pictures.
Ask the child to say the sentence and then sound out the words when writing.
The child may need help with <a, the, has> as some of the sounds may not have been taught yet.

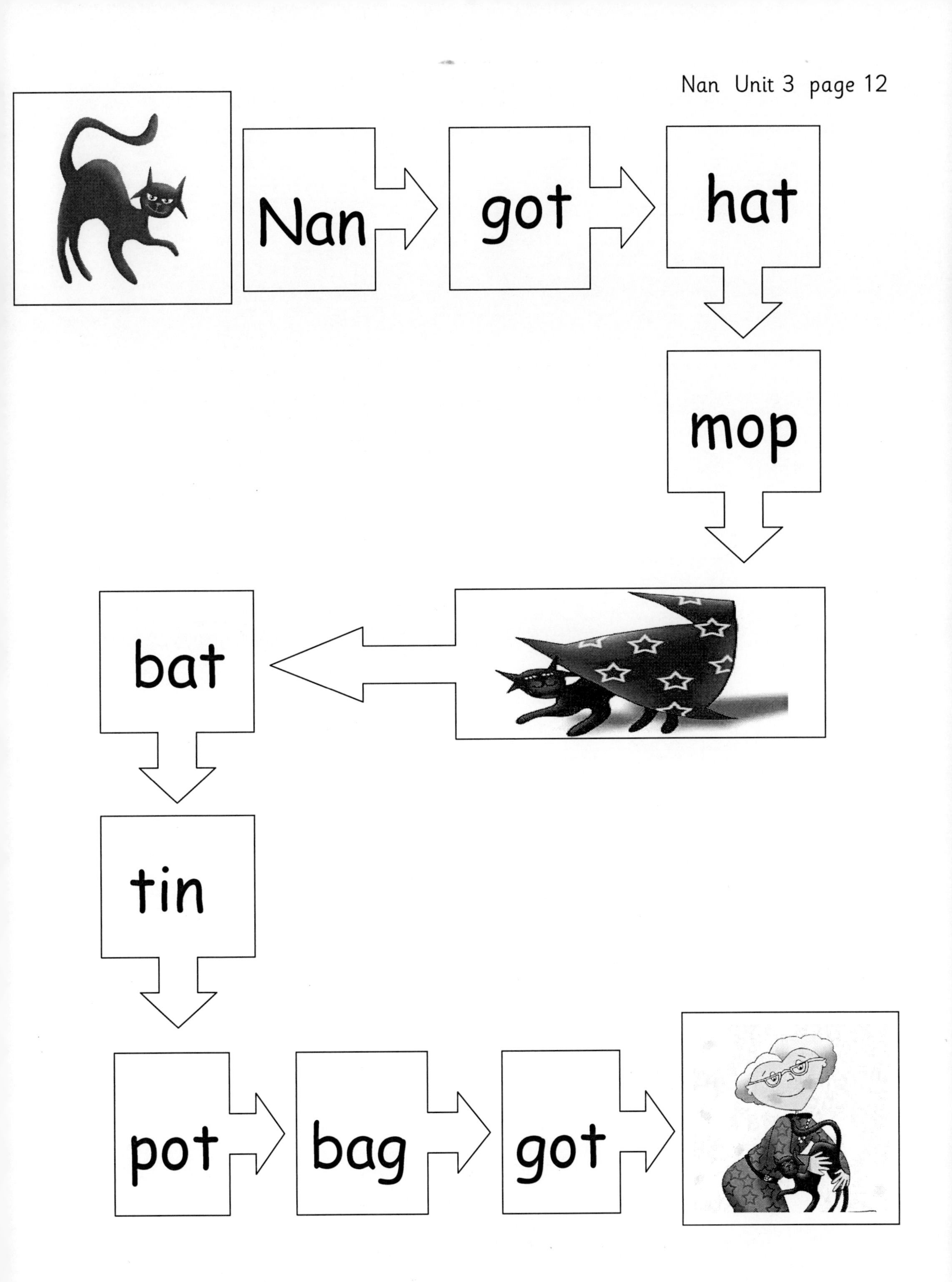

Use a dice with low numbers on it.
(1,1,2,2,0,0 or +1, +1,-1,-1,0,+2)

Dandelion Readers
from
Phonic Books Ltd

Worksheets for Unit 4 - Bad Cat

Page 1 - Sound cards d, e, f, v

Words for next 5 sheets:
van, fed, cod, bad, Dan, bed

Page 2 - Fill in the missing last sound.
Page 3 - Fill in the missing first sound.
Page 4 - Fill in the missing medial sound.
Page 5 - Fill in the missing initial and final sounds
Page 6 - Fill in all the sounds
Page 7 - Match lower case to upper case letters
Page 8 - Match upper case to lower case letters
Page 9 - Reading, cutting and pasting
Page 10 - Writing (right handers)
Page 11 - Writing (left handers)
Page 12 - Game

Each sheet has its own instructions.

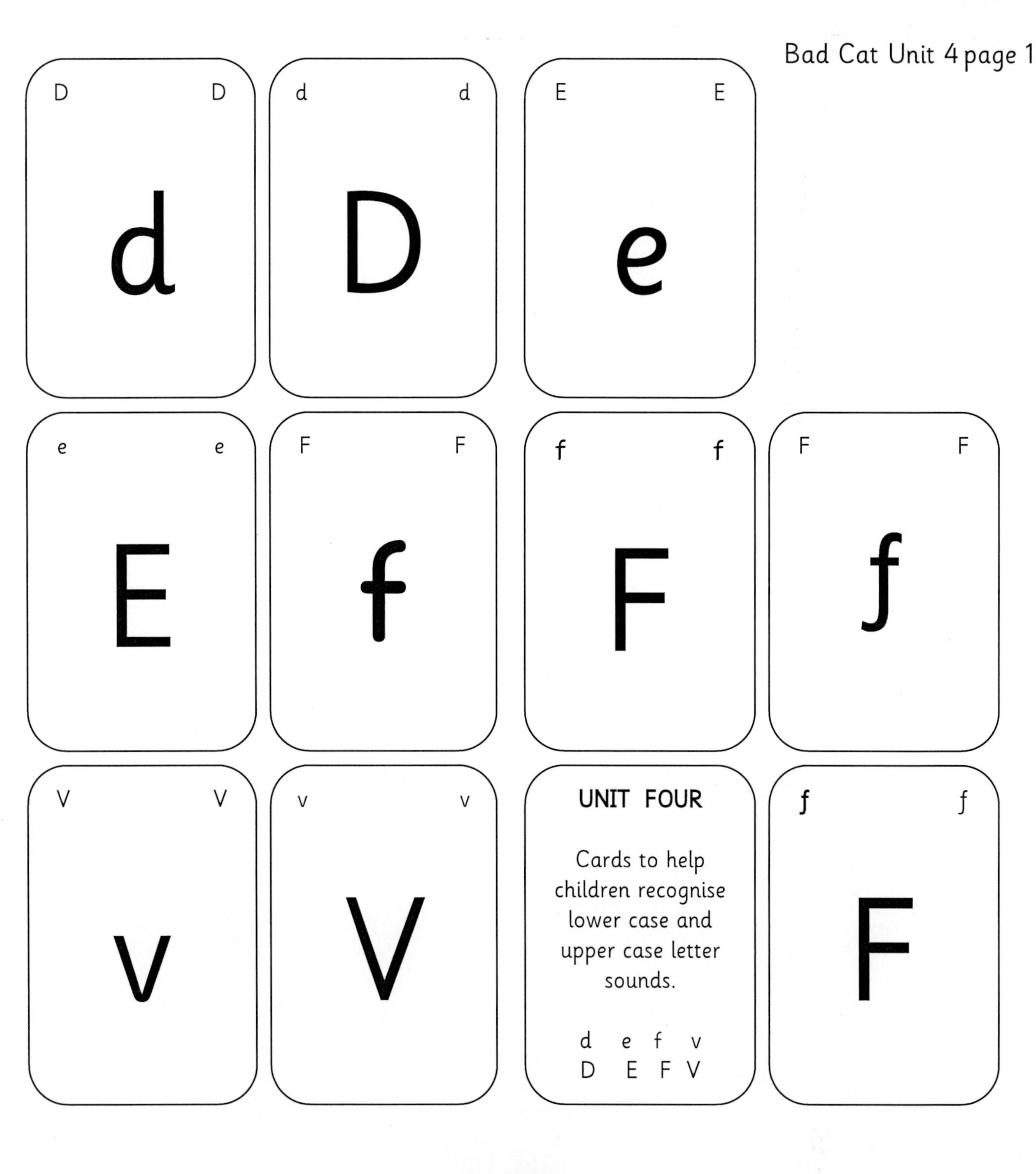

Lower case and upper case letters for Unit 4. These can be added to letters from Units 1, 2 and 3.
Photocopy the page onto card and cut out the cards. Two <f> presented to choose appropriate one.
Game 1: Say the sounds and match the pairs.
Game 2: Place the cards face down on the table. Players take turns to turn up two cards and say the sounds. If the same sound is on both cards the player keeps them. If the cards do not represent the same sound, the player replaces the cards face down and the next player has a turn. The winner is the player with the most pairs of cards!

v a _

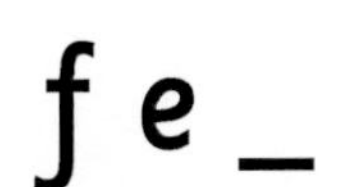

f e _

c o _

b a _

D a _

b e _

Fill in the missing final sounds.
Offer the word if the child has difficulty. Ask the child to say the sound when writing.

Name: Date:

_ a n

_ e d

_ o d

_ a d

_ a n

_ e d

Fill in the missing initial sounds.
Offer the word if the child has difficulty. Ask the child to say the sound when writing.

Name: Date:

v _ n

f _ d

c _ d

b _ d

D _ n

b _ d

Fill in the missing medial sounds.
Offer the word if the child has difficulty. Ask the child to say the sound when writing.

Name: Date:

_ a _

_ e _

_ o _

_ a _

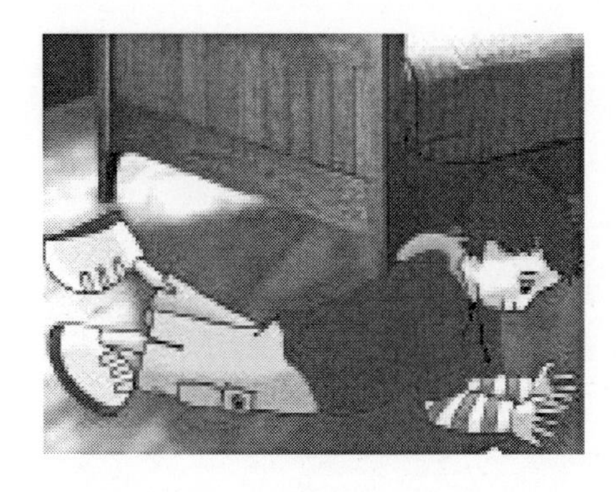

_ a _

_ e _

Fill in the missing initial and final sounds.
Offer the word if the child has difficulty. Ask the child to say the sound when writing.

Name: Date:

_ _ _   _ _ _

_ _ _   _ _ _

_ _ _   _ _ _

Fill in the missing sounds.
Offer the word if the child has difficulty. Ask the child to say the sounds when writing.

Name: Date:

D d	F f	V v	B b	E e

D	E	V

B	F

d e f b v

Match lower case letters to capital letters by cutting and pasting. Child to say the sound of the letters whilst doing the activity. <b> included from Unit 3.

Name: Date:

D d	F f	V v	B b	E e

d

e

v

b

f

D F E V B

Match capital letters to lower case letters by cutting and pasting. Child to say the sound of the letters whilst doing the activity. (<b> included from Unit 3)

Name: Date:

Dan fed the fat cat cod.

Bob sat on the hat.

Bob the cat sat on the big van.

Dan has a pet cat, Bob the cat.

Reading, cutting and pasting.

Name: Date: Bad Cat Unit 4 page 10

Dan cat fed him cod

Bob sat on van nap bad had

The the a his is

Writing - (For right handed pupil). The teacher may choose not to provide the words below the pictures.
Ask the child to say the sentence and then sound out the words when writing.
The child may need help with <the, a, his, is> as some of the sounds may not have been taught yet.

Name: Date:

Dan cat fed him cod

Bob sat on van nap bad had

The the a his is

Writing - (For left handed pupil). The teacher may choose not to provide the words below the pictures.

Ask the child to say the sentence and then sound out the words when writing.

The child may need help with <the, a , his, is> as some of the sounds may not have been taught yet.

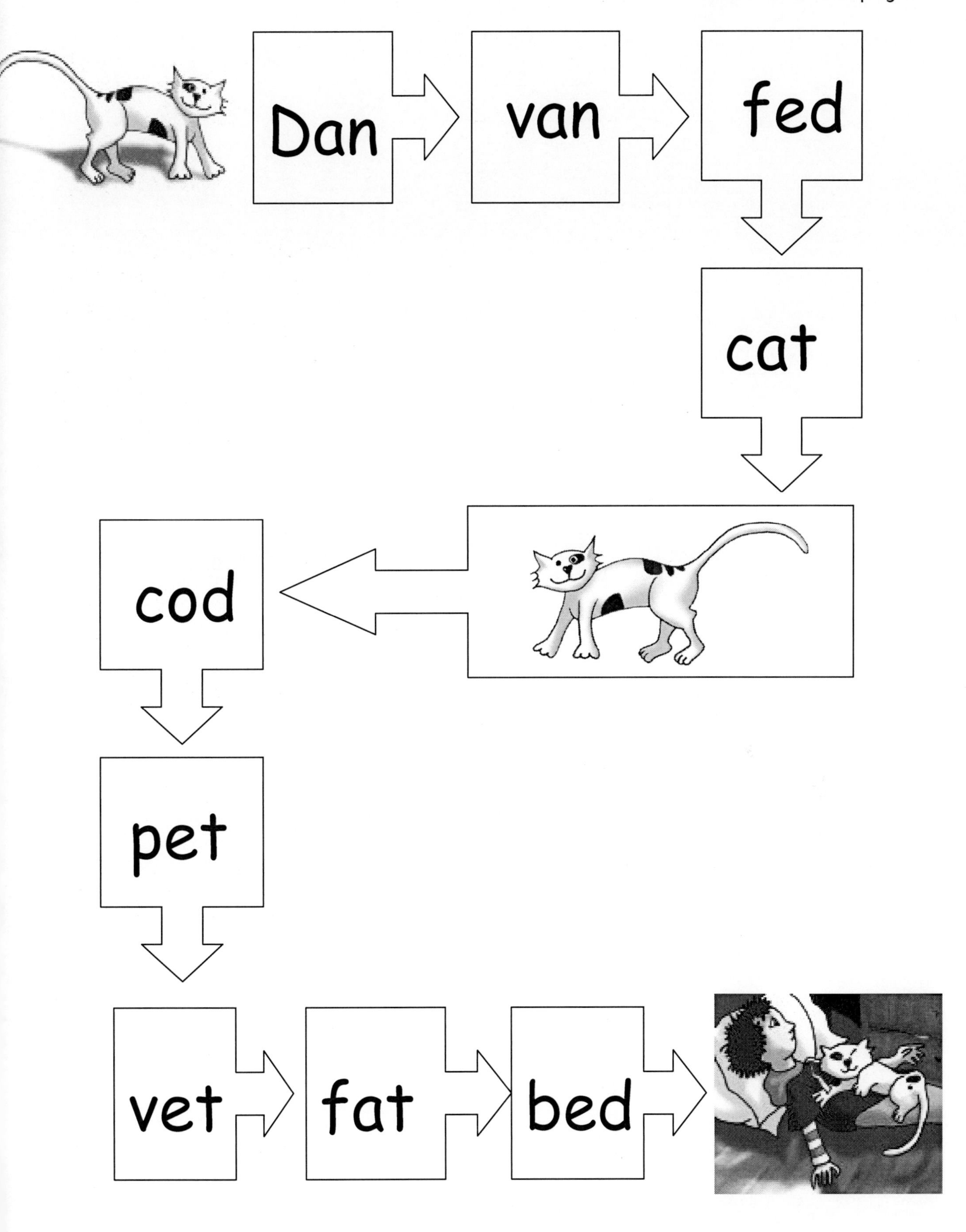

Game for unit 4. Use a dice with low numbers on it. <vet> is a new word.
(1,1,2,2,0,0 or +1,+1,-1,-1,0,+2)

Dandelion Readers
from
Phonic Books Ltd

Worksheets for Unit 5 - Bun in the Sun

Page 1 - Sound cards k, l, r, u

Words for next 5 sheets:
Kim, leg, run, lad, bun, rug

Page 2 - Fill in the missing last sound.
Page 3 - Fill in the missing first sound.
Page 4 - Fill in the missing medial sound.
Page 5 - Fill in the missing initial and final sounds
Page 6 - Fill in all the sounds
Page 7 - Match lower case to upper case letters
Page 8 - Match upper case to lower case letters
Page 9 - Reading, cutting and pasting
Page 10 - Writing (right handers)
Page 11 - Writing (left handers)
Page 12 - Game

Each sheet has its own instructions.

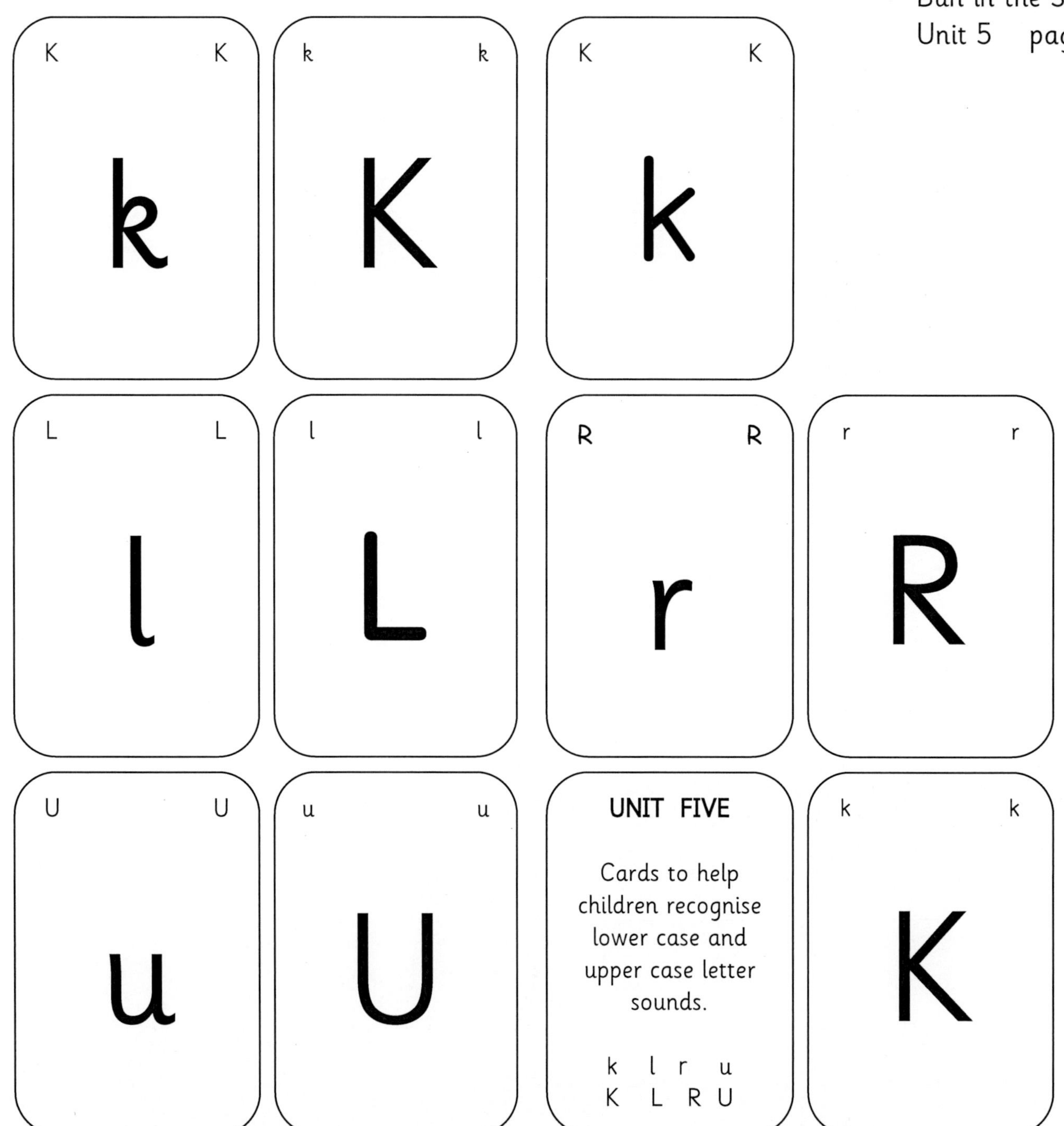

Lower case and upper case letters for Unit 5. These can be added to letters from Units 1, 2, 3 and 4. Photocopy the page onto card and cut out the cards. Two <k> presented to choose appropriate one.
Game 1: Say the sounds and match the pairs.
Game 2: Place the cards face down on the table. Players take turns to turn up two cards and say the sounds. If the same sound is on both cards the player keeps them. If the cards do not represent the same sound, the player replaces the cards face down and the next player has a turn. The winner is the player with the most pairs of cards!

Name: Date: Bun in the Sun
Unit 5 page 2

K i _

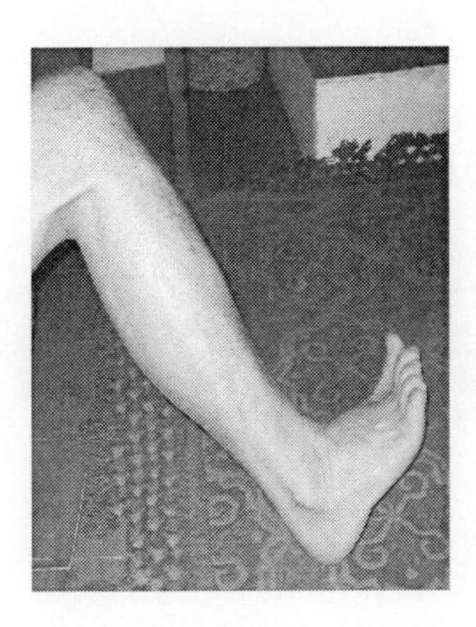

l e _

r u _

l a _

b u _

r u _

Fill in the missing final sounds.
Offer the word if the child has difficulty. Ask the child to say the sound when writing.

Name: Date:

_i m

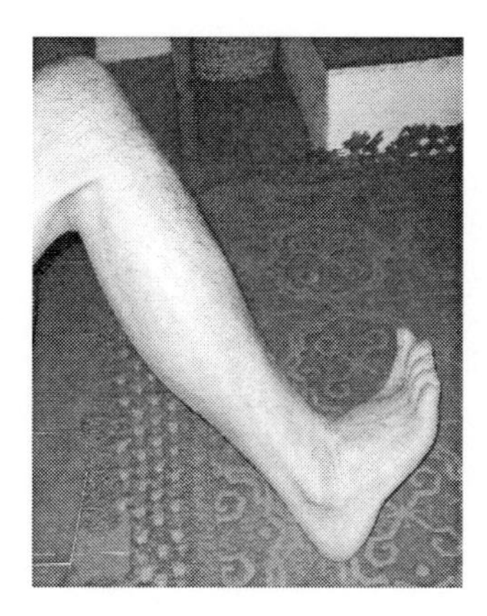

_e g

_u n

_a d

_u n

_u g

Fill in the missing initial sounds.
Offer the word if the child has difficulty. Ask the child to say the sound when writing.

Name: Date:

K _ m

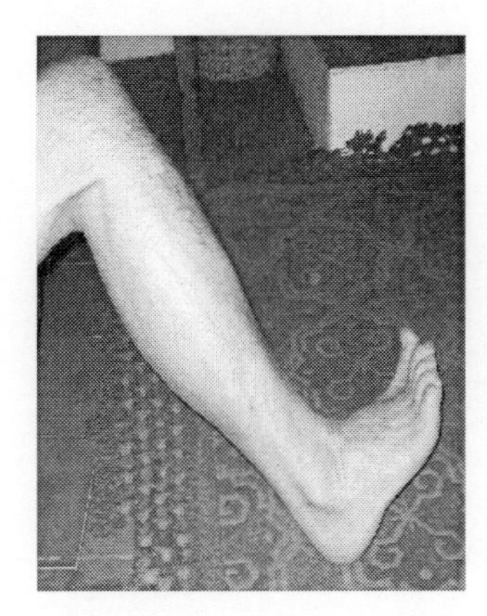

l _ g

r _ n

l _ d

b _ n

r _ g

Fill in the missing medial sounds.
Offer the word if the child has difficulty. Ask the child to say the sound when writing.

Name: Date:

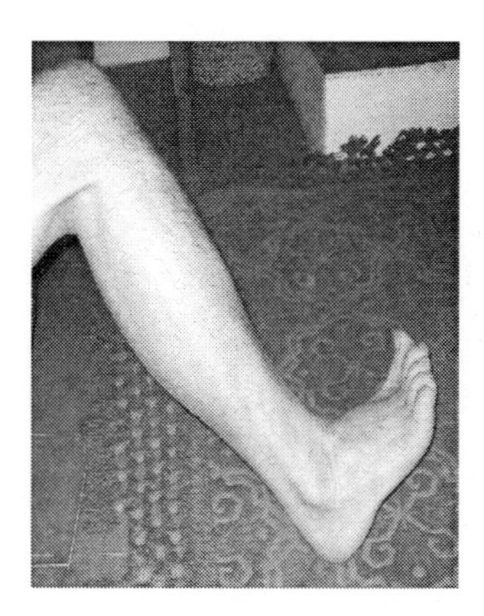

_ i _ _ e _

_ u _ _ a _

_ u _ _ u _

Fill in the missing initial and final sounds.
Offer the word if the child has difficulty. Ask the child to say the sounds when writing.

Name: Date:

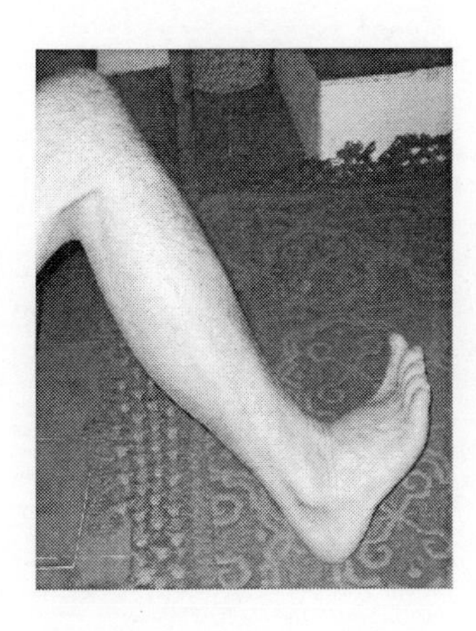

_ _ _

_ _ _

_ _ _

_ _ _

_ _ _

_ _ _

Fill in the missing sounds.
Offer the word if the child has difficulty. Ask the child to say the sounds when writing.

Name: Date:

K k	L l	U u	R r	V v

R	K	V

U		L

r	u	l	k	v

Match lower case letters to capital letters by cutting and pasting. Child to say the sound of the letters whilst doing the activity. <v> included from Unit 4.

Name: Date:

U	L	K	V	R
u	l	k	v	r

r	k	v

u	l

U R L K V

Match capital letters to lower case letters by cutting and pasting. Child to say the sound of the letters whilst doing the activity. (<v> included from Unit 4)

Name: 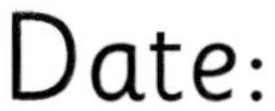 Date:

A lad on a rug has a big fat bun.

Pip and Kim sit on a log.

The lad got Kim in a cup.

Pip and Kim got on the bun.

Reading, cutting and pasting.

Name: Date:

Kim log sit on Pip and
lad bun fat big rug got
A a has and

Writing - (For right handed pupil). The teacher may choose not to provide the words below the pictures.
Ask the child to say the sentence and then sound out the words when writing.
The child may need help with <a, has, and> as some of the sounds may not have been taught yet.

Name: Date:

Kim log sit on Pip and
lad bun fat big rug got

A a has and

Writing - (For left handed pupil.) The teacher may choose not to provide the words below the pictures.
Ask the child to say the sentence and then sound out the words when writing.
The child may need help with <a, has, and> as some of the sounds may not have been taught yet.

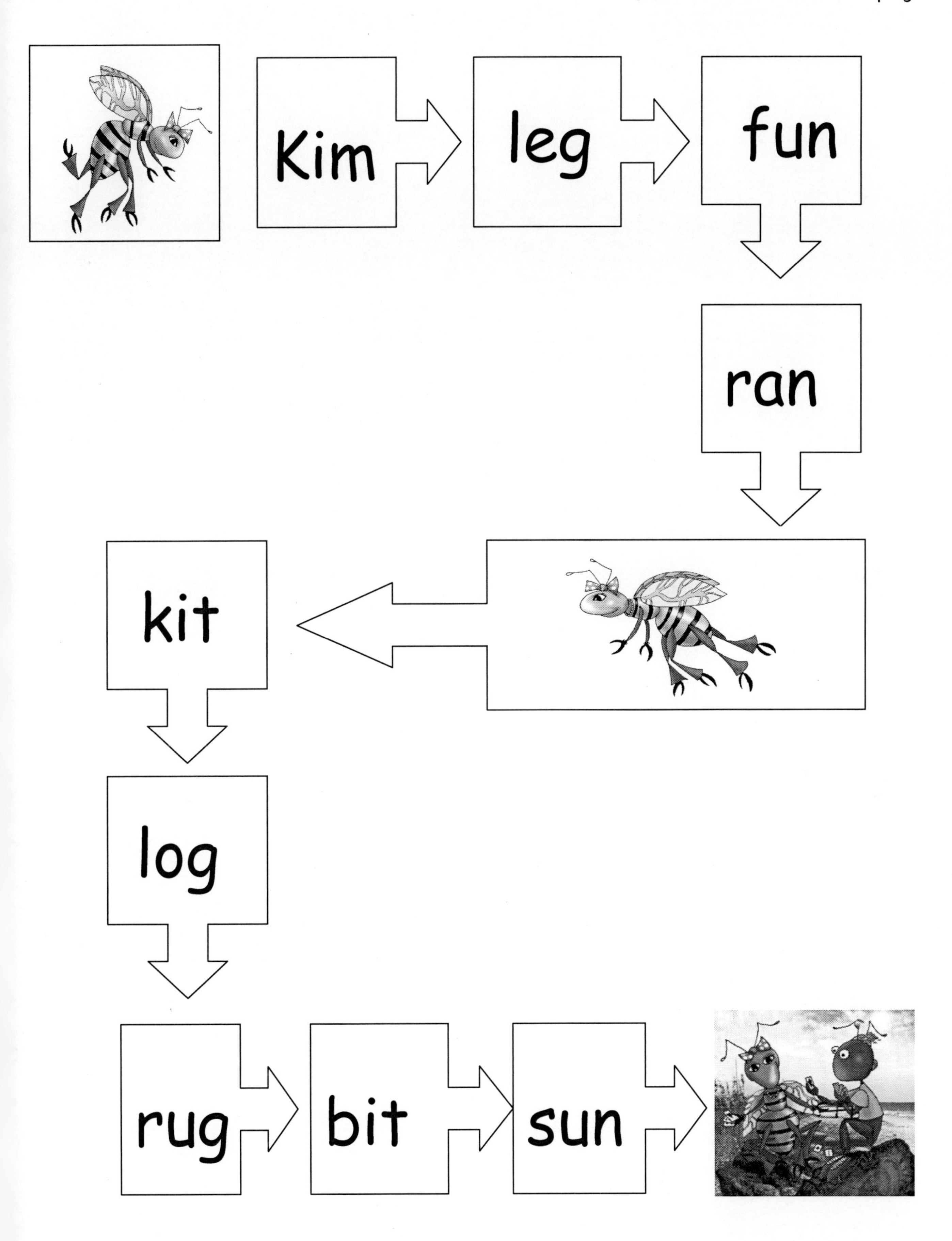

Game for unit 5. Use a dice with low numbers on it. <kit> is a new decodable word.
(1,1,2,2,0,0 or +1, +1,-1,-1,0,+2)

Dandelion Readers
from
Phonic Books Ltd

Worksheets for Unit 6 - Zig and Zog

Page 1 - Sound cards j, w, z

Words for next 5 sheets:
zip, wet, jam, win, Zog, jet

Page 2 - Fill in the missing last sound.
Page 3 - Fill in the missing first sound.
Page 4 - Fill in the missing medial sound.
Page 5 - Fill in the missing initial and final sounds
Page 6 - Fill in all the sounds
Page 7 - Match lower case to upper case letters
Page 8 - Match upper case to lower case letters
Page 9 - Reading, cutting and pasting
Page 10 - Writing (right handers)
Page 11 - Writing (left handers)
Page 12 - Game

Each sheet has its own instructions.

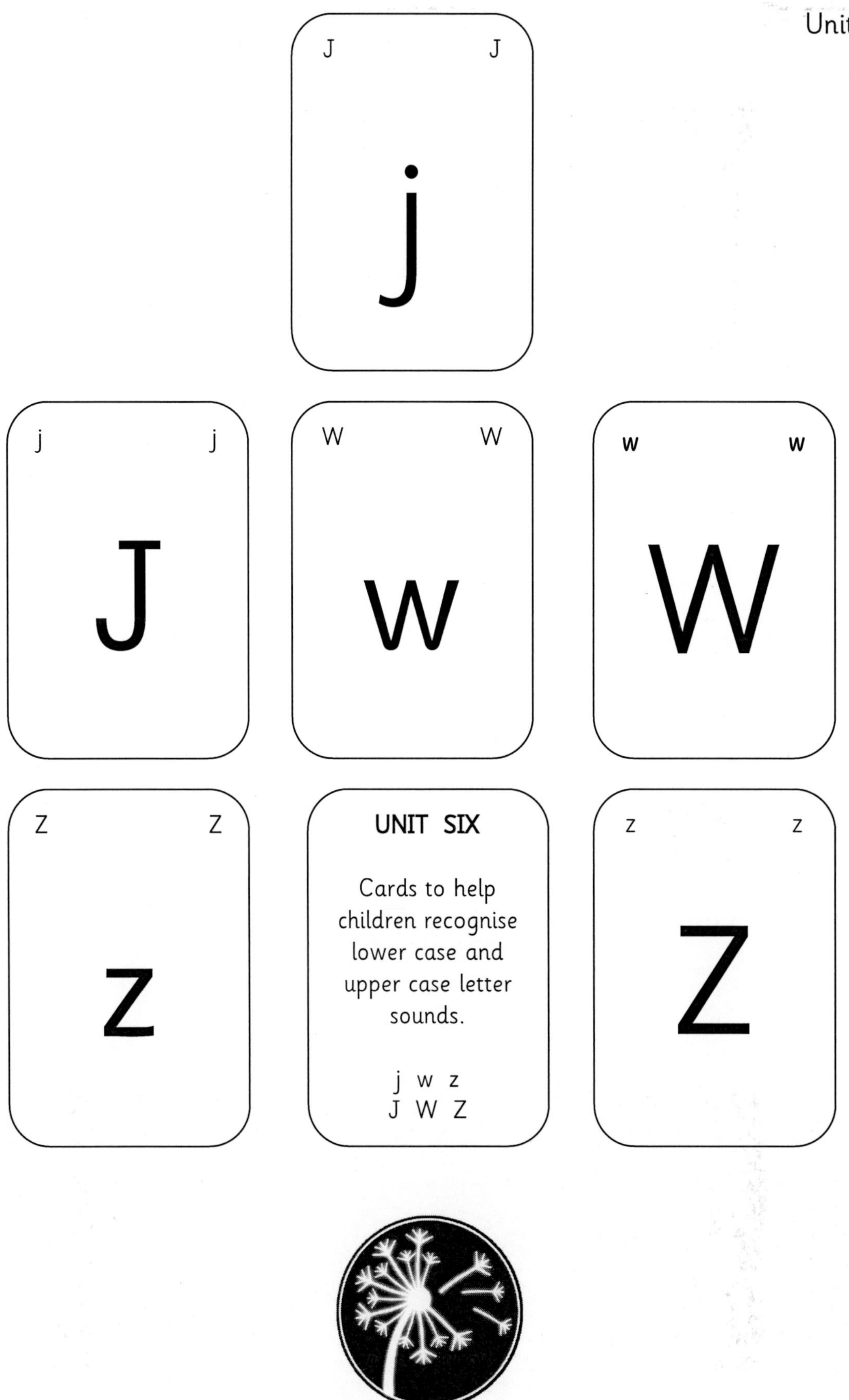

Lower case and upper case letters for Unit 6. These can be added to letters from Units 1, 2, 3, 4 and 5.
Photocopy the page onto card and cut out the cards.
Game 1: Say the sounds and match the pairs.
Game 2: Place the cards face down on the table. Players take turns to turn up two cards and say the sounds. If the same sound is on both cards the player keeps them. If the cards do not represent the same sound, the player replaces the cards face down and the next player has a turn. The winner is the player with the most pairs of cards!

Name: Date:

z i _ **w e _**

j a _ **w i _**

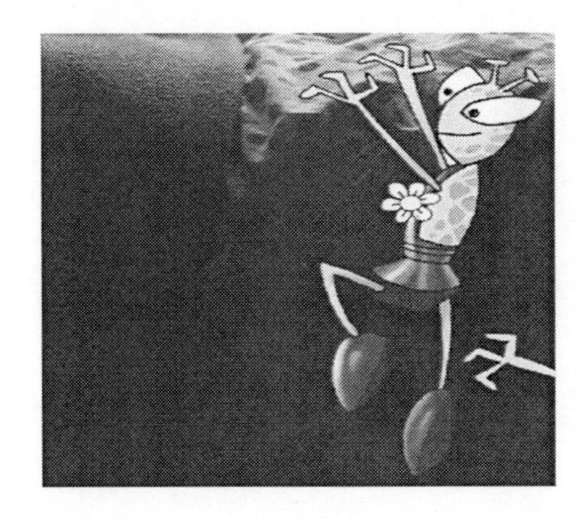

Z o _ **j e _**

Fill in the missing final sounds.
Give the word if the child has difficulty. Ask the child to say the sound when writing.

Name: Date:

_ i p

_ e t

_ a m

_ i n

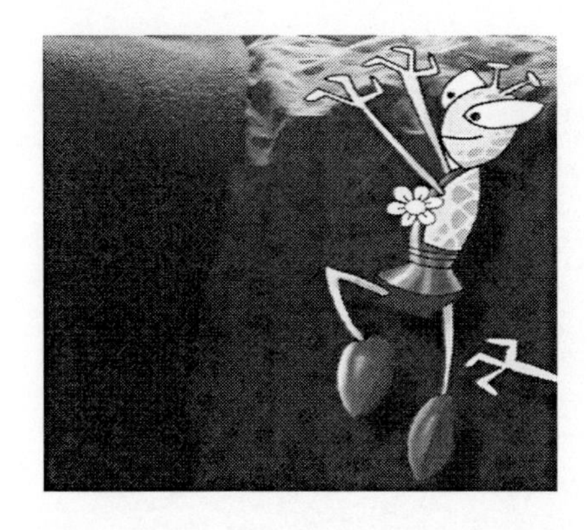

_ o g

_ e t

Fill in the missing initial sounds.
Give the word if the child has difficulty. Ask the child to say the sound when writing.

Name: Date:

z _ p

w _ t

j _ m

w _ n

Z _ g

j _ t

Fill in the missing medial sounds.
Give the word if the child has difficulty. Ask the child to say the sound when writing.

Name: Date:

_ i _

_ e _

_ a _

_ i _

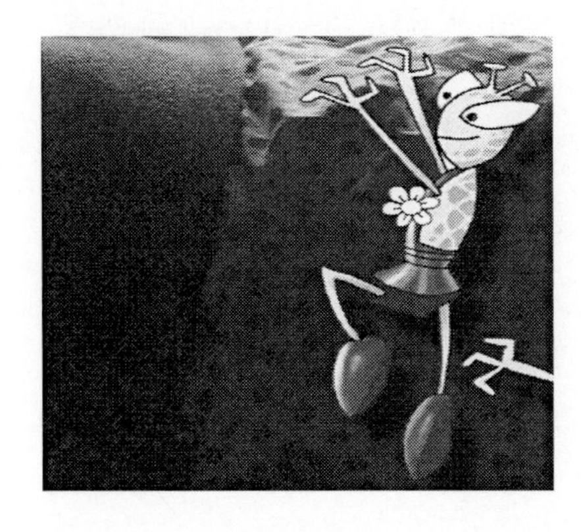

_ o _

_ e _

Fill in the missing initial and final sounds.
Give the word if the child has difficulty. Ask the child to say the sound when writing.

Name: Date:

_ _ _   _ _ _

_ _ _   _ _ _

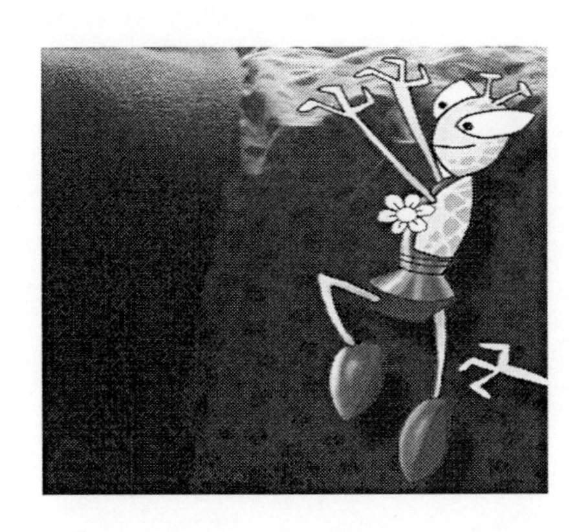

_ _ _   _ _ _

Fill in the missing sounds.
Give the word if the child has difficulty. Ask the child to say the sound when writing.

Name: Date:

J	B	W	D	Z
j	b	w	d	z

W	B	Z

D	J

b j w d z

Unit 6 - Match lower case letters to capital letters by cutting and pasting. Child to say the sound of the letters whilst doing the activity. <b> and <d> have been included.

Name: Date:

J	D	Z	B	W
j	d	z	b	w

w

b

z

d

j

J W D B Z

Unit 6 - Match capital letters to lower case letters by cutting and pasting. Child to say the sound of the letters whilst doing the activity. <b> and <d> have been included.

Name:  Date:

Liz is in bed. Zig and Zog get up.

Zig ran to the red bus. It had jam on it.

Zog sat on a big wet jet.

Zig and Zog run and jog. Zog ran in to Zig.

Reading, cutting and pasting. The word 'into' has been split so as not to introduce a two syllable word at this stage.

Name: Date:

Zog wet jet sat on big

Zig bus jam not fun it had

was the

Writing. (For right handed pupils). The teacher may choose not to provide the words below the pictures.

Ask the child to say the sentence and then sound out the words when writing.

The child may need help with <was, the> as some of the sounds may not have been taught yet.

Name: Date:

Zog wet jet sat on big
Zig bus jam not fun it had
was the

Writing. (For left handed pupils). The teacher may choose not to provide the words below the pictures.
Ask the child to say the sentence and then sound out the words when writing.
The child may need help with <was, the> as some of the sounds may not have been taught yet.

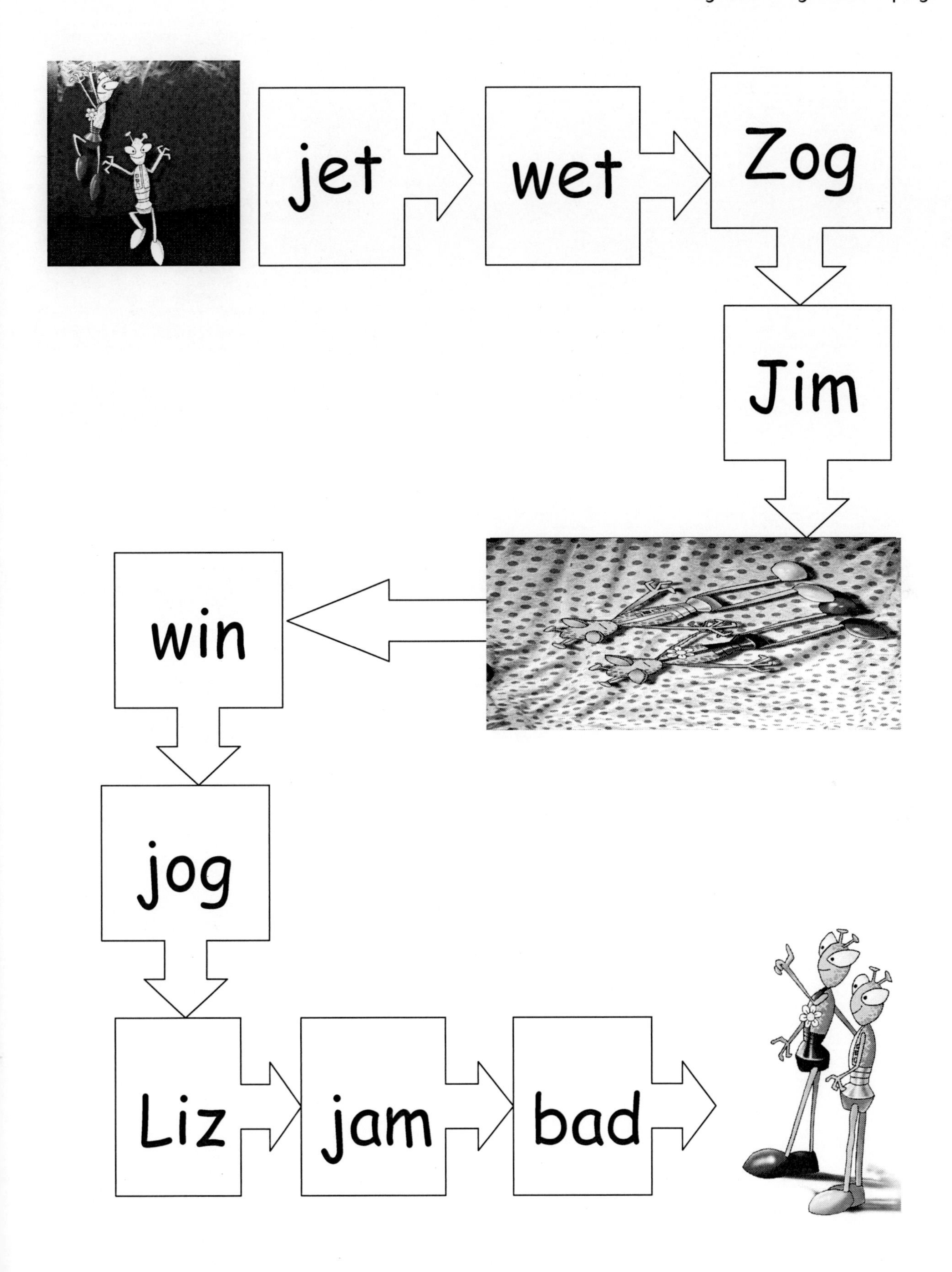

Game for unit 6 book 1 'Zig and Zog'. Use a dice with low numbers on it. Included are some new decodable words.
(1,1,2,2,0,0 or +1,+1,-1,-1,0,+2)

Dandelion Readers
from
Phonic Books Ltd

Worksheets for Unit 7 - Bob is not Well

Page 1 - Sound cards x, y, ff, ll, ss

Words for next 5 sheets:
yes, box, six, yell, cuff, mess

Page 2 - Fill in the missing last sound.
Page 3 - Fill in the missing first sound.
Page 4 - Fill in the missing medial sound.
Page 5 - Fill in the missing initial and final sounds
Page 6 - Fill in all the sounds
Page 7 - Match lower case to upper case letters
Page 8 - Match upper case to lower case letters
Page 9 - Reading, cutting and pasting
Page 10 - Writing (right handers)
Page 11 - Writing (left handers)
Page 12 - Game

Each sheet has its own instructions.

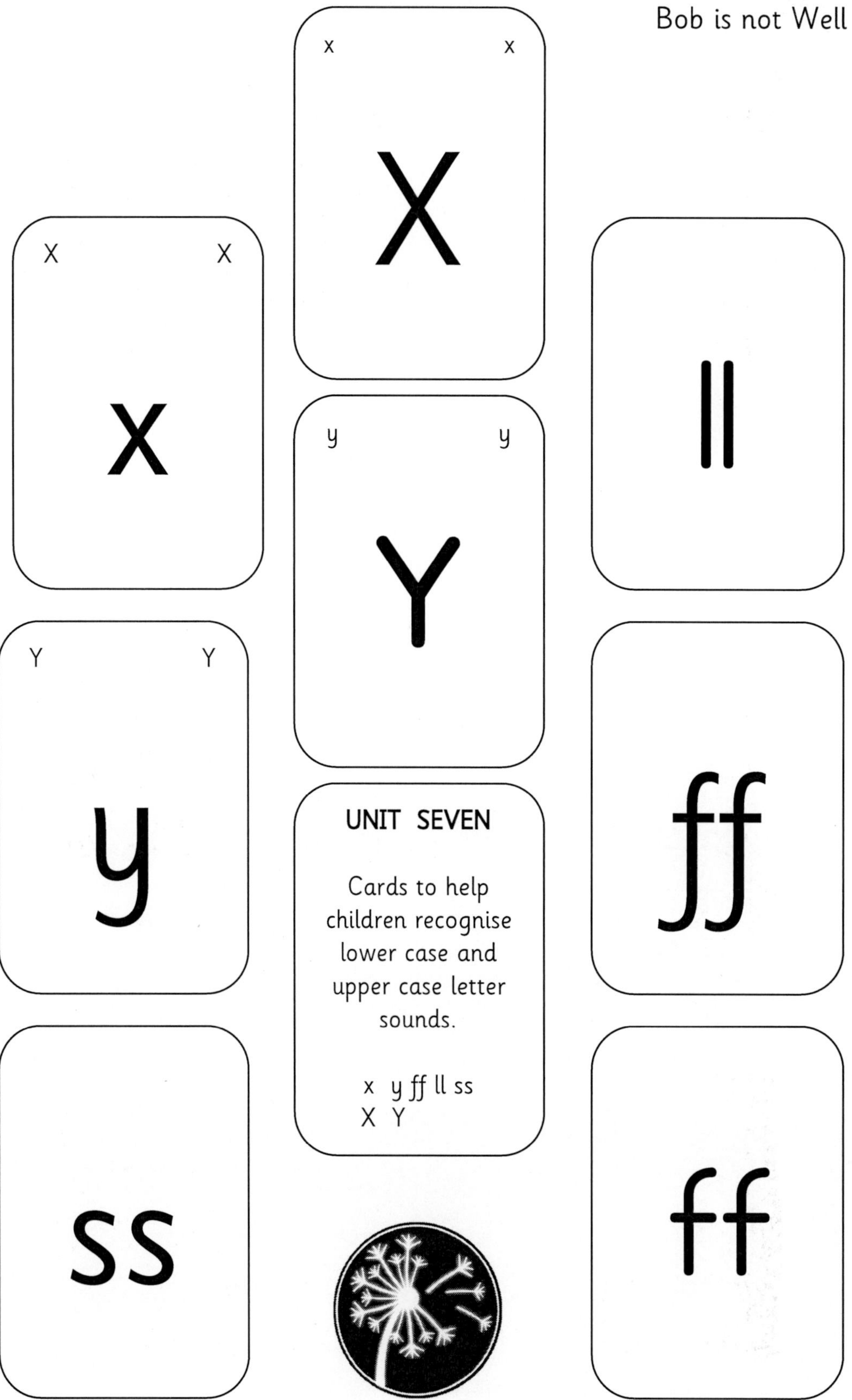

Lower case and upper case letters for Unit 7. These can be added to letters from Units 1, 2, 3, 4, 5, and 6. <ff> <ll> and <ss> have been included as they might be useful to explain that two identical letters can represent one sound. Photocopy the page onto card twice and cut out the cards.

Game 1: Say the sounds and match the pairs.

Game 2: Place the cards face down on the table. Players take turns to turn up two cards and say the sounds. If the same sound is on both cards the player keeps them. If the cards do not represent the same sound, the player replaces the cards face down and the next player has a turn. The winner is the player with the most pairs of cards!

Name: Date:

ye_

bo_

si_

ye_

cu_

me_

Fill in the missing final sound. (<ff> <ll>, <ss> represent one sound.)
Give the word if the child has difficulty. Ask the child to say the sound when writing it.

Name: Date:

_ e s

_ o x

_ i x

_ e ll

_ u ff

_ e ss

Fill in the missing initial sound. (<ff> <ll>, <ss> represent one sound.)
Give the word if the child has difficulty. Ask the child to say the sound when writing it.

Name: Date:

y _ s

b _ x

s _ x

y _ ll

c _ ff

m _ ss

Fill in the missing medial sound. (<ff> <ll>, <ss> represent one sound.)
Give the word if the child has difficulty. Ask the child to say the sound when writing it.

Name: Date:

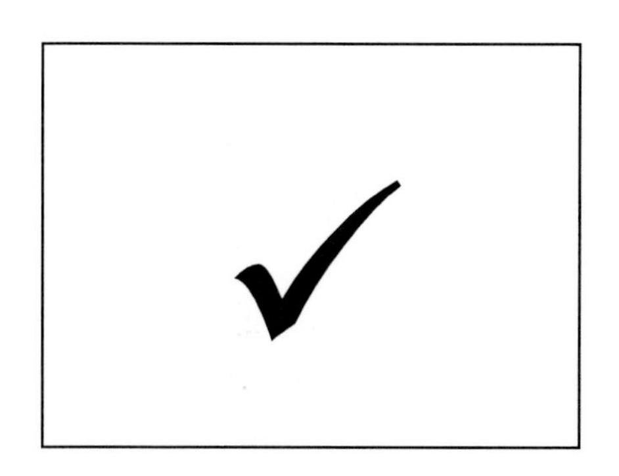

_ e _

_ o _

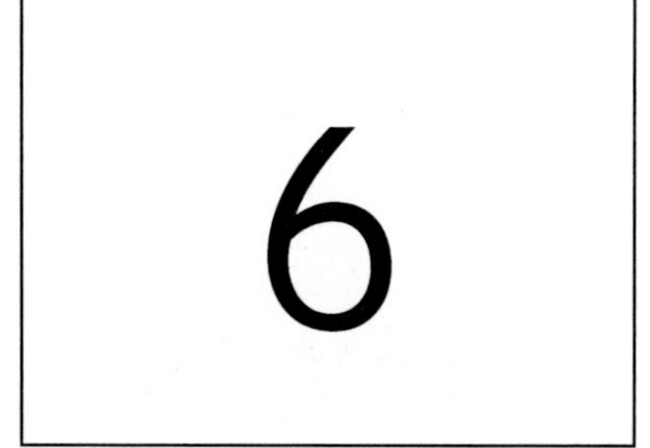

_ i _

_ e _

_ u _

_ e _

Fill in the missing initial and final sounds. (<ff> <ll>, <ss> represent one sound.)
Give the word if the child has difficulty. Ask the child to say the sound when writing it.

Name: Date: Bob is not Well Unit 7 page 6

_ _ _

_ _ _

_ _ _

_ _ _

_ _ _

_ _ _

Fill in the missing sounds. (<ff> <ll>, <ss> represent one sound.)
Give the word if the child has difficulty. Ask the child to say the sound when writing it.

Name: Date: Bob is not Well Unit 7 page 7

X	B	P	D	Y
x	b	p	d	y

B	X	P

Y	D

p d x b y

Unit 7 - Match lower case letters to capital letters by cutting and pasting. Child to say the sound of the letters whilst doing the activity. <b> <d> and <p> have been included.

Name: Date:

P	D	X	B	Y
p	d	x	b	y

b

y

p

d

x

Y	P	D	B	X

Unit 7 - Match capital letters to lower case letters by cutting and pasting. Child to say the sound of the letters whilst doing the activity. <b> <d> and <p> have been included.

Name: Date:

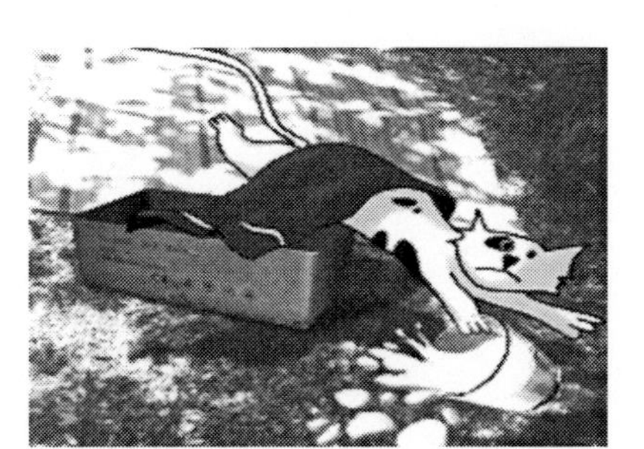

Bob can fit in a box. The box is his bed.

I will mix a pill in a cup. Bob is not well.

Bob is well. Bob ran off.

Bob hit the cup and it fell. Yes, a big mess.

Reading, cutting and pasting.

Name: Date:

Bob box can in fit .

will cup mix in pill

I a the

Writing. (For right handed pupils). The teacher may choose not to provide the words below the pictures.
Ask the child to say the sentence and then sound out the words when writing.
The child may need help with <I, a, the> as some of the sounds may not have been taught yet.

Name: Date:

Bob box can in fit .
will cup mix in pill
I a the

Writing. (For left handed pupils). The teacher may choose not to provide the words below the pictures.
Ask the child to say the sentence and then sound out the words when writing.
The child may need help with <I, a, the > as some of the sounds may not have been taught yet.

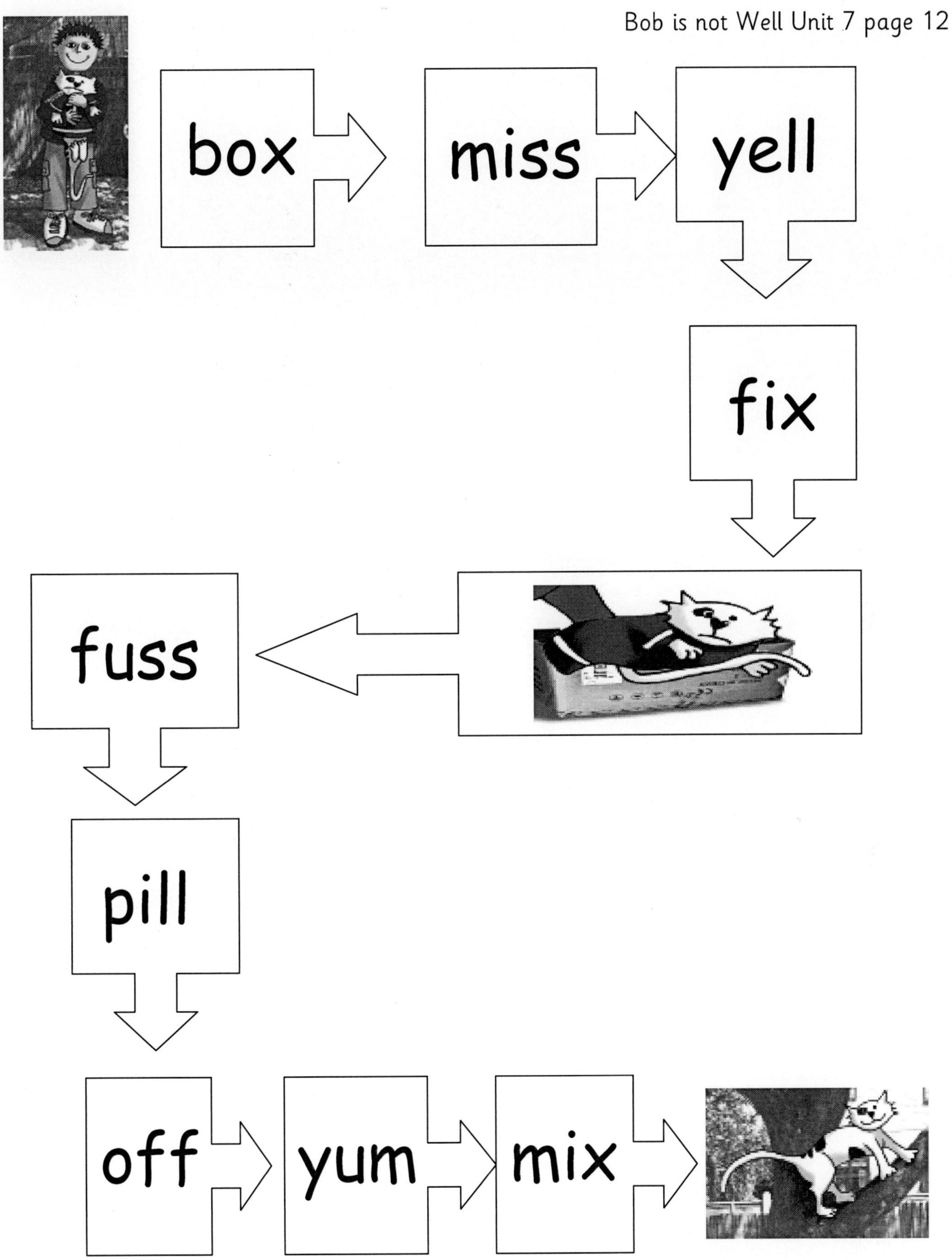

Use a dice with low numbers on it. Included are some new decodable words.
(1,1,2,2,0,0 or +1,+1,-1,-1,0,+2)

Dandelion Readers
from
Phonic Books Ltd

Worksheets for Unit 8 - The Lost Box CVCC

Words for next 6 sheets:
rest, hunt, tips, lost, hand, sink

Page 1 - Fill in the missing last sound.
Page 2 - Fill in the missing third sound.
Page 3 - Fill in the missing second sound.
Page 4 - Fill in the missing second and fourth sounds
Page 5 - Fill in the missing first and third sounds.
Page 6 - Fill in all the sounds.
Page 7 - Reading, cutting and pasting (right handers)
Page 8 - Reading, cutting and pasting (left handers)
Page 9 – Free writing (right handers)
Page 10 – Free writing (left handers)
Page 11 - Game – 4 in a row.

Each sheet has its own instructions.

Name: Date:

r e s _

h u n _

t i p _

l o s _

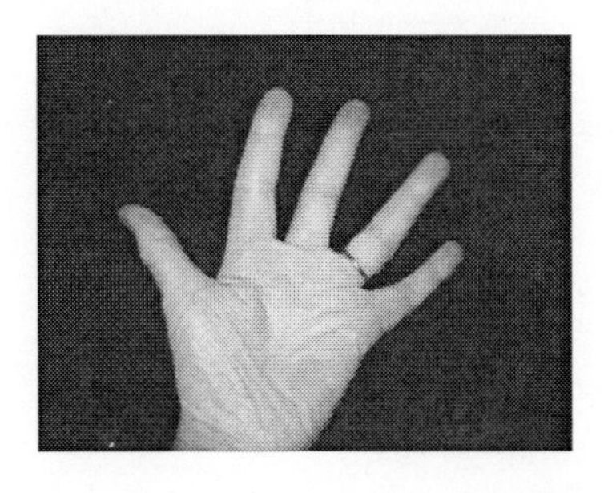

h a n _

s i n _

Fill in the missing final sound in these four sound words. Give the word if the child has difficulty. Ask the child to say the sound when writing it.

Name: Date:

r e _ t

h u _ t

t i _ s

l o _ t

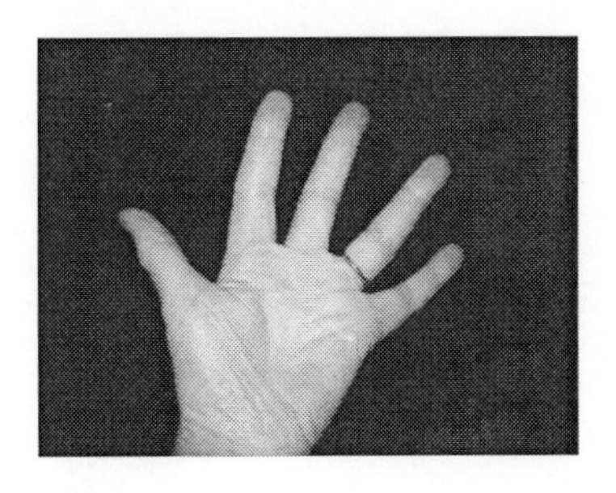

h a _ d

s i _ k

Fill in the missing third sound in these four sound words. Give the word if the child has difficulty.
Ask the child to say the sound when writing it.

Name: Date:

r _ s t

h _ n t

t _ p s

l _ s t

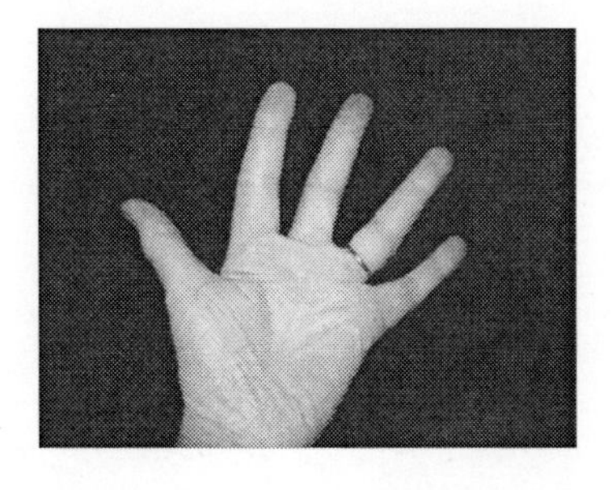

h _ n d

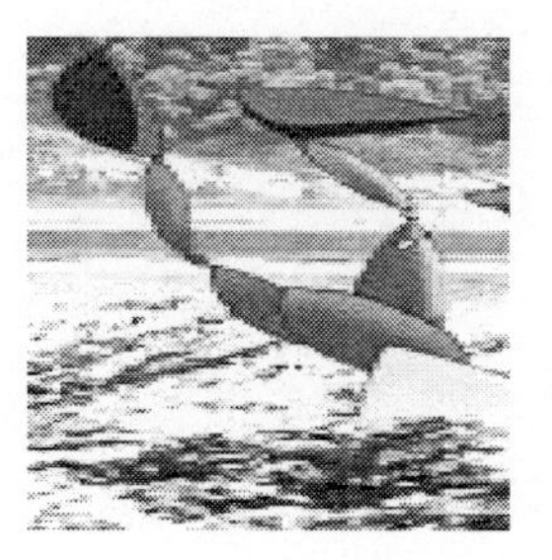

s _ n k

Fill in the missing vowel sound in these four sound words. Give the word if the child has difficulty.
Ask the child to say the sound when writing it.

Name: Date:

r _ s _

h _ n _

t _ p _

l _ s _

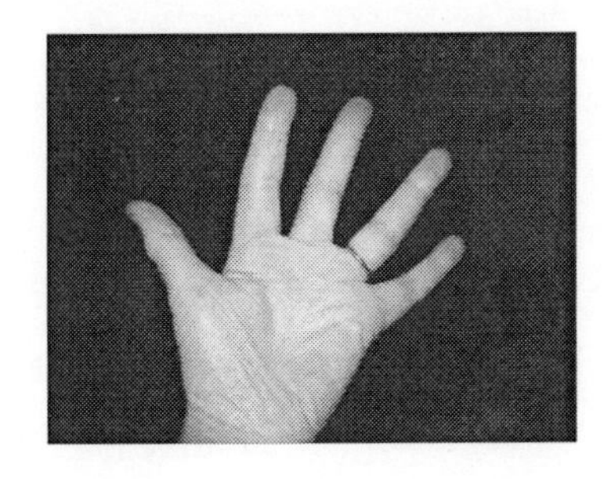

h _ n _

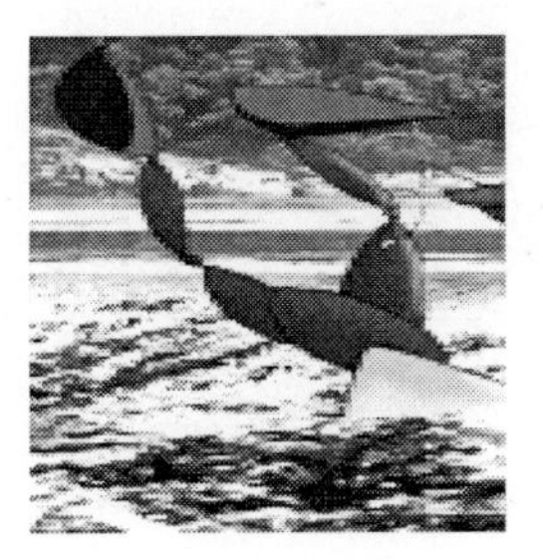

s _ n _

Fill in the missing second and last sounds in these four sound words. Give the word if the child has difficulty. Ask the child to say the sound when writing it.

Name: Date:

_ e _ t

_ u _ t

_ i _ s

_ o _ t

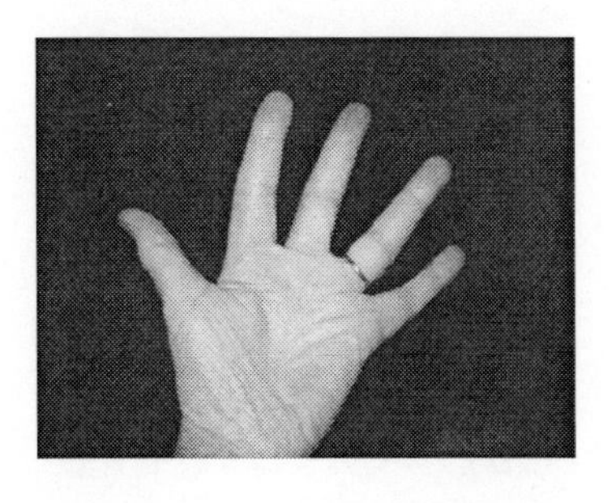

_ a _ d

_ i _ k

Fill in the missing first and third sounds in these four sound words. Give the word if the child has difficulty. Ask the child to say the sound when writing it.

Name: Date:

_ _ _ _

_ _ _ _

_ _ _ _

_ _ _ _

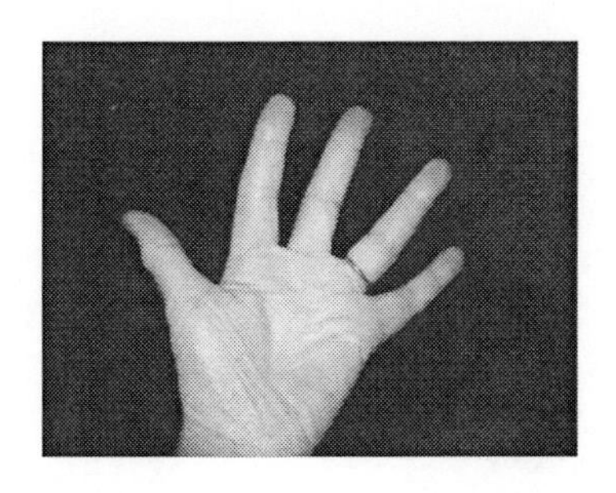

_ _ _ _

_ _ _ _

Fill in the missing sounds in these four sound words. Give the word if the child has difficulty. Ask the child to say the sound when writing it.

Name: Date:

The logs tip and
Tess and Pip fell in.

Tess and Pip went on a
hunt for the lost box.

Tess held on to the logs
and held Pip's hand.

Reading, cutting and pasting. (For right handed pupils)

Name: Date:

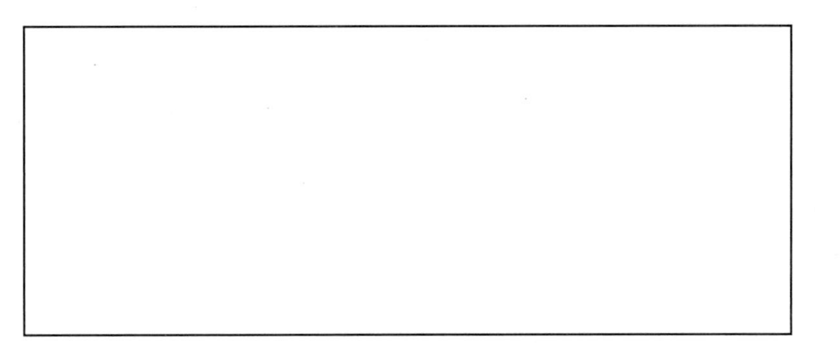

The logs tip and Tess and Pip fell in.

Tess and Pip went on a hunt for the lost box.

Tess held on to the logs and held Pip's hand.

Reading, cutting and pasting. (For left handed pupils)

Name: Date:

The, the, is, for, to

Free Writing with picture cue. (For right handed writers.)

Name: Date:

The, the, is, for, to

Free Writing with picture cue. (For left handed writers.)

CVCC 4 in a Row

logs	went	hunt	lost	tips
held	sank	hand	soft	rest
lost	tips	logs	went	hunt
soft	rest	sank	held	hand
hunt	logs	went	lost	tips
held	hand	rest	sank	soft
lost	hunt	logs	went	tips

Unit 8 - Two different sets of coloured counters are needed. Two players take it in turns to read the word and put a counter on the word. The winner is the first to get four counters in a row.
Play four games. When a game is won the winner places a counter on a dandelion.

Dandelion Readers
from
Phonic Books Ltd

Worksheets for Unit 9 - Flip and Flop Slip
CCVC

Words for next 6 sheets:
plug, flap, twig, grip, stop, slip

Page 1 - Fill in the missing first sound.
Page 2 - Fill in the missing second sound.
Page 3 - Fill in the missing third sound.
Page 4 - Fill in the missing first and third sounds
Page 5 - Fill in the missing second and fourth sounds.
Page 6 - Fill in all the sounds.
Page 7 - Reading, cutting and pasting (right handers)
Page 8 - Reading, cutting and pasting (left handers)
Page 9 – Free writing (right handers)
Page 10 – Free writing (left handers)
Page 11 - Game – 4 in a row.

Each sheet has its own instructions.

Name: Date:

_lug

_lap

_wig

_rip

_top

_lip

Fill in the missing initial sound in these four sound words. Give the word if the child has difficulty.
Ask the child to say the sound when writing it.

Name: Date:

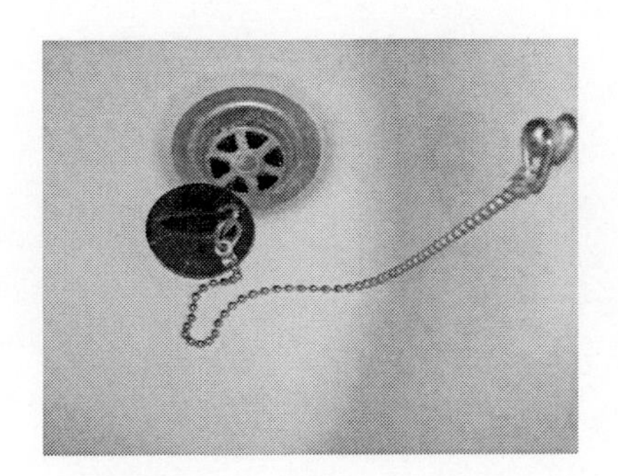

p _ u g

f _ a p

t _ i g

g _ i p

s _ o p

s _ i p

Fill in the missing second sound in these four sound words. Give the word if the child has difficulty.
Ask the child to say the sound when writing it.

Name: Date:

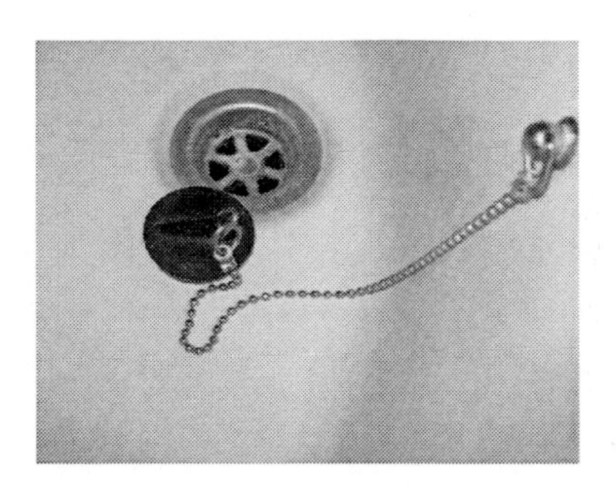

p l _ g

f l _ p

t w _ g

g r _ p

s t _ p

s l _ p

Fill in the missing third sound in these four sound words. Give the word if the child has difficulty.
Ask the child to say the sound when writing it.

Name: Date:

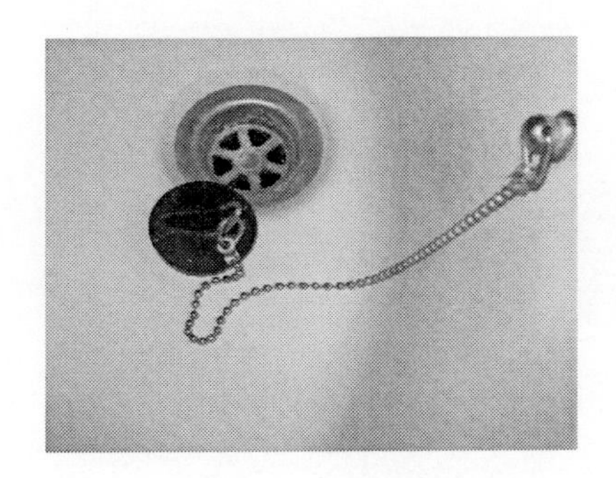

_ l _ g

_ l _ p

_ w _ g

_ r _ p

_ t _ p

_ l _ p

Fill in the missing first and third sound in these four sound words. Give the word if the child has difficulty. Ask the child to say the sound when writing it.

Name: Date:

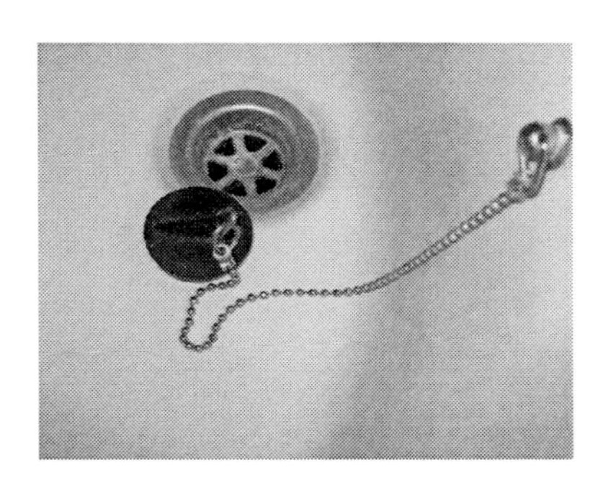

p _ u _

f _ a _

t _ i _

g _ i _

s _ o _

s _ i _

Fill in the missing second and last sounds in these four sound words. Give the word if the child has difficulty. Ask the child to say the sound when writing it.

Name: Date: Flip and Flop Slip Unit 9 page 6

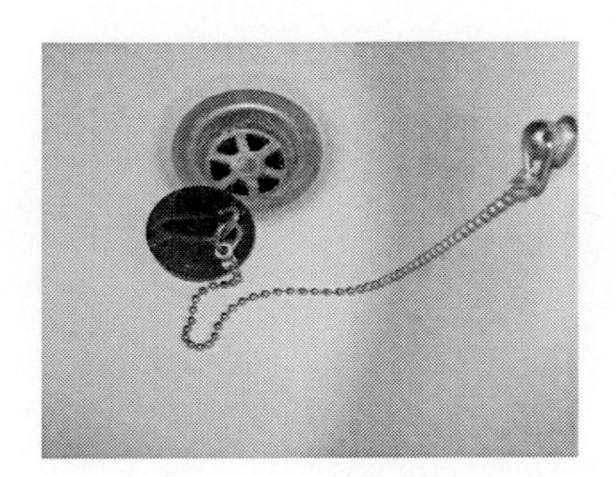

_ _ _ _ _ _ _ _

_ _ _ _ _ _ _ _

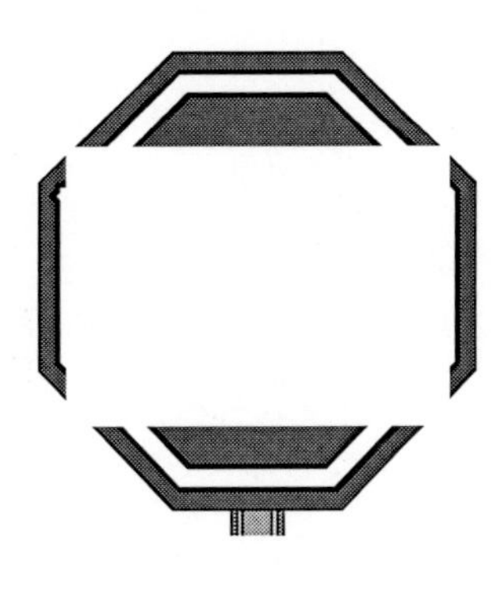

_ _ _ _ _ _ _ _

Fill in the missing sounds in these four sound words. Give the word if the child has difficulty. Ask the child to say the sound when writing it.

Name: Date:

Flip is a twin and
Flop is a twin.

Flip lost his grip and
Flop slid off.

Flip and Flop jump and
flap, flap, flap.

Reading, cutting and pasting. (For right handed pupils)

Name: Date:

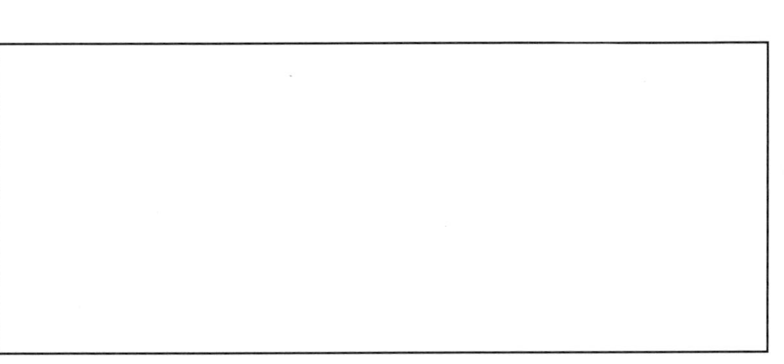

Flip is a twin and Flop is a twin.

Flip lost his grip and Flop slid off.

Flip and Flop jump and flap, flap, flap.

Reading, cutting and pasting. (For left handed pupils)

Name: Date:

The, the, is, for, to

Free Writing with picture cue. (For right handed writers.)

Name: Date:

The, the, is, for, to

Free writing with picture cue. (For left handed writers.)

CCVC 4 in a Row Flip and Flop Slip Unit 9 page 11

Unit 9 – Two different sets of coloured counters are needed. Two players take it in turns to read the word and put a counter on the word. The winner is the first to get four counters in a row.
Play four games. When a game is won the winner places a counter on a dandelion.

Dandelion Readers
from
Phonic Books Ltd

Worksheets for Unit 10 - The Stink CCVCC

Words for first 6 sheets:
stink, stump, skunk, stamp, crabs, trunk

Page 1 - Fill in the missing first two sounds
Page 2 - Fill in the missing last two sounds
Page 3 - Fill in the missing first and fourth sounds
Page 4 - Fill in the missing second and fifth sounds
Page 5 - Fill in the missing second and fourth sounds.
Page 6 - Fill in all the sounds
Page 7 - Reading, cutting and pasting (right handers)
Page 8 - Reading, cutting and pasting (left handers)
Page 9 - Free writing
Page 10 - Game – 4 in a row.

Each sheet has its own instructions.

Name: Date: The Stink Unit 10 page 1

_ _ i n k

_ _ u m p

_ _ u n k

_ _ a m p

_ _ a b s

_ _ u n k

Fill in the missing first two sounds in these five sound words. Give the word if the child has difficulty. Ask the child to say the sound when writing it.

Name: Date: The Stink Unit 10 page 2

s t i _ _

s t u _ _

s k u _ _

s t a _ _

c r a _ _

t r u _ _

Fill in the missing fourth and final sounds in these five sound words. Give the word if the child has difficulty. Ask the child to say the sound when writing it.

Name: Date:

_ t i _ k

_ t u _ p

_ k u _ k

_ t a _ p

_ r a _ s

_ r u _ k

Fill in the missing first and fourth sounds in these five sound words. Give the word if the child has difficulty. Ask the child to say the sound when writing it.

Name: Date:

s _ i n _

s _ u m _

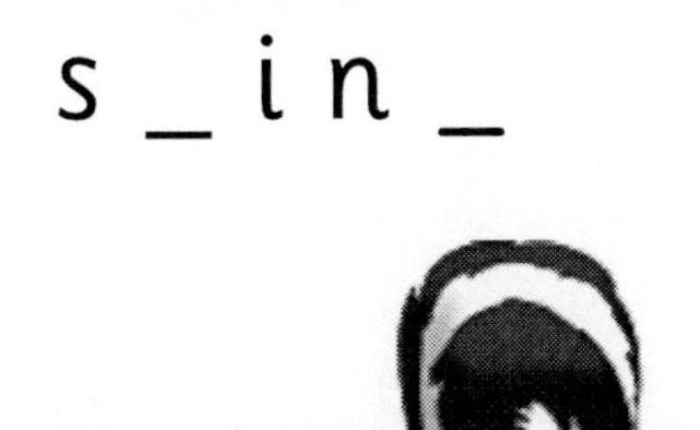

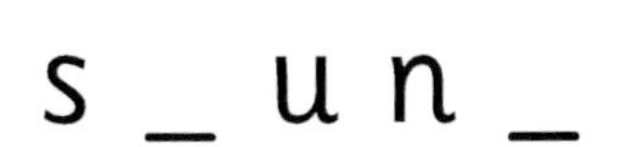

s _ u n _

s _ a m _

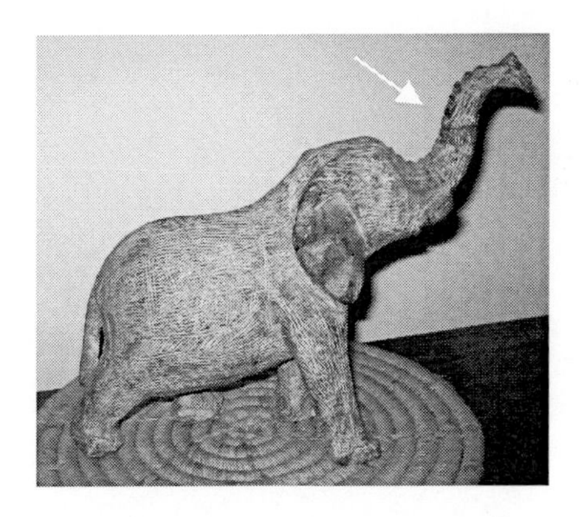

c _ a b _

t _ u n _

Fill in the missing second and last sounds in these five sound words. Give the word if the child has difficulty. Ask the child to say the sound when writing it.

Name: Date:

s _ i _ k

s _ u _ p

s _ u _ k

s _ a _ p

c _ a _ s

t _ u _ k

Fill in the missing second and fourth sounds in these five sound words. Give the word if the child has difficulty. Ask the child to say the sound when writing it.

Name: Date: The Stink Unit 10 page 6

_ _ _ _ _

_ _ _ _ _

_ _ _ _ _

_ _ _ _ _

_ _ _ _ _

_ _ _ _ _

Fill in the missing sounds in these five sound words. Give the word if the child has difficulty. Ask the child to say the sound when writing it.

Name: Date:

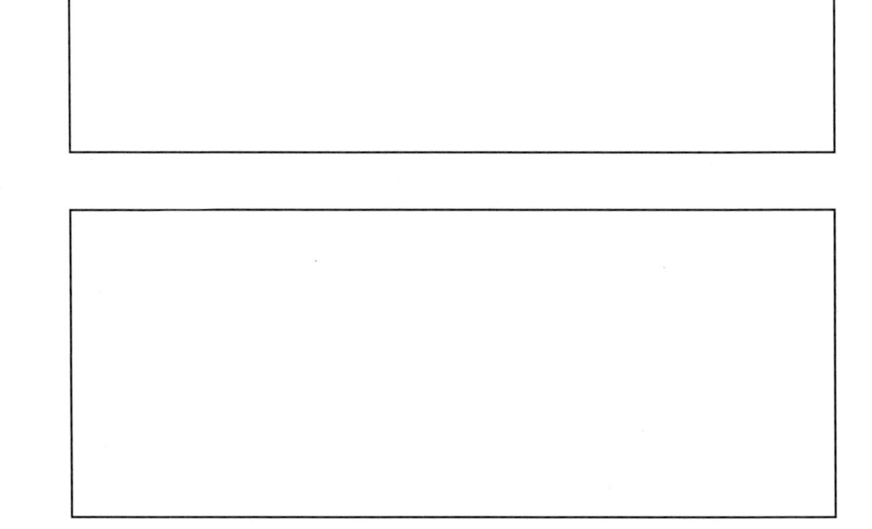

Alf and Frank smelt a big stink. Is it from the pond?

Frank and Alf crept up to the stump. The stink was from Punk.

Alf and Frank slept well in the tent in the camp.

Reading, cutting and pasting. (For right handed pupils)

Name: Date:

Alf and Frank smelt a big stink. Is it from the pond?

Frank and Alf crept up to the stump. The stink was from Punk.

Alf and Frank slept well in the tent in the camp.

Reading, cutting and pasting. (For left handed pupils)

Name: Date:

Free writing.

CCVCC

4 in a Row

drink	scamp	bland	spent	grand
twins	crest	glint	frisk	twist
stand	print	blink	skunk	slept
stump	scalp	craft	grunt	stamp
blond	trunk	blend	tramp	stank
blunt	slept	crisp	frost	brisk

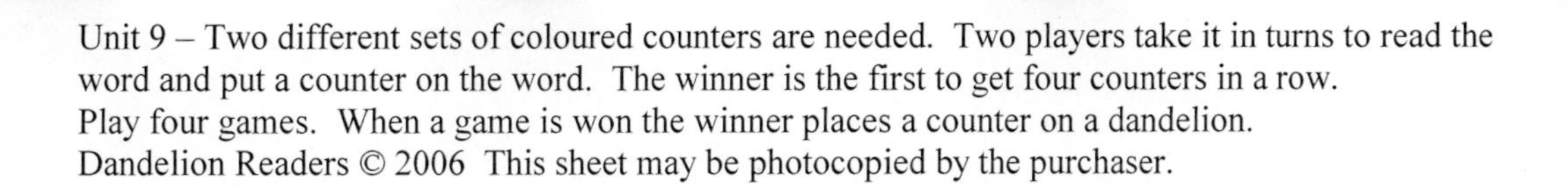

Unit 9 – Two different sets of coloured counters are needed. Two players take it in turns to read the word and put a counter on the word. The winner is the first to get four counters in a row.
Play four games. When a game is won the winner places a counter on a dandelion.